WORDS TO GO!

Book F

WORDS TO KNOW!

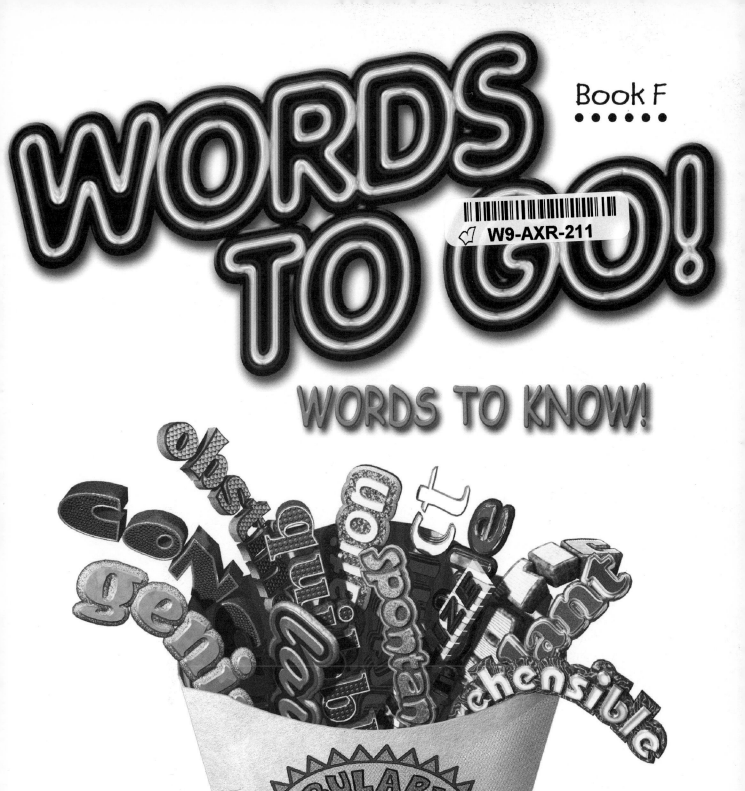

VOCABULARY WORKBOOK

Perfection Learning®

Publisher

Perfection Learning® Corporation

Editorial Director   **Julie A. Schumacher**

Editorial Consultant   **Terry Ofner**

Art Director   **Randy Messer**

Concept, Writing, and Design

Sense and Nonsense, Inc.

Writer   **Jan Gleiter**

Designer   **Paul H. Thompson**

5153 North Clark Street, Suite 307
Chicago, Illinois 60640-6823
Tel 1-773-728-0779

78989

Printed in the U.S.A.

14 15 16 17 PP 16 15 14 13 12

HD ISBN-13: 978-0-7659-1636-7 ISBN-10: 0-7569-1636-4
PB ISBN-13: 978-0-7891-5473-6 ISBN-10: 0-7891-5473-0

TABLE OF CONTENTS

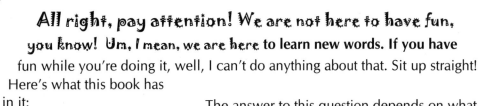

All right, pay attention! We are not here to have fun, you know! Um, I mean, we are here to learn new words. If you have fun while you're doing it, well, I can't do anything about that. Sit up straight! Here's what this book has in it:

- **Lots of useful words.** You may already know some of them. For the words you don't know, this book tells you their most common meanings and uses them in sample sentences. Stop chewing that gum.

- **Pronunciations.** The words are respelled in a way that's easy to understand. And there are none of those sĭl'ē sĭm'bəlz that are harder to figure out than the words themselves!

- **Exercises.** Of course, there are exercises! It's a workbook! There are also "Know-How" lessons to give you some know-how.

- **Jokes and riddles.** Some of them are really lame. Some of them are really funny. (Some of them, to be honest, are just beyond me.)

Here's what you need:
- a pen or pencil
- some lined paper
- a sense of humor

If you're missing any of these things, go to the shopping mall right now. Hee-hee! I'm just kidding. Sit down!

Now, let's be serious for a moment. There are fifteen words in each lesson in this book, there are five lessons in each unit, and there are six units. So how many words are in this book?

  a. 15   c. 1556
  b. 450   d. all of them

The answer to this question depends on what *words* means. This book uses **Word** or **Words** when it means the words you are supposed to learn. For example, when it asks you to write the **Word** that best completes a sentence, you will write one of the fifteen words from the lesson's word list. You will *not* fill in just any old word that completes the sentence, even if it's your favorite word in the whole world.

So the answer is 450 **Words.** You will have a great vocabulary! And you will have fun! Or else.

Now read what three of my former students said about **Words to Go!**

Fernetta Foxtrotter, *Cook, Age 37*
They didn't have **Words to Go!** when I was in school. So now when I want to say something is, you know, really big, all I can say is "It's really big" or "It's really, really big" or maybe "That thing is as big as something that's really, really, really big."

Carrie Cabinfever, *Student, 7th Grade*
For me, **Words to Go!** was an immense help.

Stevie Swansong, *Student, 12th Grade*
I cannot ascertain quite how to convey to you how passionate I feel about **Words to Go!** This immensely beneficial book enabled me to alter my vocabulary from that of a mere ignoramus to that of an eloquent word enthusiast.

And after you finish this book, you'll understand what Stevie was talking about! Or else.

Mrs. Mimi Morgenstern teaches sixth grade at Fiddlebrook Middle School in Pezville, Pennsylvania.

Know-How

Base Words and Roots

A word may have only one part, such as *help,* or it may have several parts, such as *unhelpfulness.* Every word, no matter how long, has a main part. This main part may be a "base word," or it may be a "root."

A **base word** is a complete word that can be used to build other words. The base word in *friendship, friendless, befriend,* and *unfriendly* is *friend.* Even though *end* can also be found in these words, it isn't the base word. That's because the words are not built from *end* and have nothing to do with *end!*

When a word part is added at the end of the base word, the spelling at the end may change a little. For example, *nap* is the base word in *napping, pollute* is the base word in *pollution,* and *mercy* is the base word in *merciful.*

Exercise A

Find the base word in each of these words and write it on the line.

1. freedom   _____

2. knowledge   _____

3. worthless   _____

4. exploration   _____

5. glorious   _____

6. unstoppable   _____

7. foolishness   _____

8. restrengthen   _____

9. courageous   _____

10. unhappiness   _____

A word **root** is the main part of some words. It has a special meaning, but it is not a complete word. For example, the root of *science* is *sci,* which means "to know." Roots are trickier than base words because they aren't whole words, and they come from other languages. Many of the roots of English words come from Greek and Latin.

This table shows five common roots and their meanings. Use this information to complete Exercise B.

ROOT	MEANING	EXAMPLES
cycl	circle	bicycle, cycling
ject	throw	inject, reject
ped	foot	pedal, pedestrian
port	carry	portable, transport
vac	empty	vacant, vacuum

Exercise B

Use the table to answer the questions.

_____ 11. What does a *pedometer* measure?
    A. steps   B. noise   C. vibrations

_____ 12. How do the winds in a *cyclone* move?
    A. up and down   B. straight ahead   C. around and around

_____ 13. Which of the following is a common *projectile*?
    A. a tire   B. an arrow   C. a suitcase

_____ 14. Where would you *portage* a canoe?
    A. across land   B. down a river   C. in a boat store

_____ 15. If people *evacuate* a building, what do they do?
    A. build it   B. leave it   C. crowd into it

Exercise C

Write the base word or the root for each of these words.

16. ejection   _____

17. enlargement   _____

18. distrustful   _____

19. vacuous   _____

20. pedestal   _____

Exercise D

Read each of these sentences. On the short line, write the base word or root for the underlined word. On the longer line, write down a possible meaning for the underlined word.

21. Eating well, exercising, and getting enough sleep are all important for healthy <u>maturation</u>.

   _____   _____

22. Some planes have a seat that will <u>eject</u> the pilot before a crash.

   _____   _____

23. Terry is such a <u>braggart</u> that no one can stand to listen to him.

   _____   _____

24. We ate well while staying at the lake because of its <u>plenteous</u> fish.

   _____   _____

25. Birds and humans are the only animals that are <u>bipeds</u>.

   _____   _____

Know-How

Prefixes

A **prefix** is a word part added to the beginning of a root or base word to change its meaning in some way. The change made by a prefix may be small. After all, the difference between a *bi*cycle and a *tri*cycle is just one wheel. However, the change may be huge. An *un*friendly person is very different from a friendly one.

Sometimes prefixes are added to whole words that you already know. You may not recognize the new word that has been created, but you can figure it out. To do that, first you need to realize that the word contains a prefix.

This table shows some common prefixes and their meanings. Use this information to complete all of the exercises in this lesson.

PREFIX	MEANING	EXAMPLES
en	to make or cause	enlarge, encourage
il, im, in, ir	not	illegal, immature, inability, irregular
mis	bad	misfortune, mistreat
pre	before	precaution, prepay
re	again	rewrite, refresh
re	back	recall, repay

Here's a helpful hint. In many cases, the meaning of the prefix will make more sense if you put it after the word in your mind.

Examples: prepay: "pay before" (not "before pay")

rewrite: "write again" (not "again write")

repay: "pay back" (not "back pay")

Exercise A

These are common words that contain prefixes. Write the prefix on the line next to each word.

1. refill   _____

2. enclose   _____

3. prefix   _____

4. misread   _____

5. impure   _____

Exercise B

Write the letter of the word or phrase that means the same thing as each word on the left.

____ 6. entrap   A. unmoving

____ 7. restitch   B. crime

____ 8. misdeed   C. plan

____ 9. immobile   D. mend

____ 10. prearrange   E. capture

Exercise C

Add a prefix to the given base word to form the new word that belongs in the blank.

11. *admit* The usher would not _____ me because I didn't have my ticket when I returned from the snack stand.

12. *state* Honest people don't _____ the facts; they tell the truth.

13. *judge* It can be a mistake to _____ a situation. Don't make up your mind before you have the facts.

14. *press* I tried to _____ my laughter, but it was hard to hold it back.

15. *able* I hope that studying will _____ me to pass the test.

Exercise D

Combine the prefix and the word that is shown to make a new word. Then write a sentence that uses the new word.

16. in + action _____

_____

_____

17. mis + inform _____

_____

_____

18. im + moral _____

_____

_____

19. en + rich _____

_____

_____

20. pre + war _____

_____

_____

Know-How

A **suffix** is a word part added to the end of a root or base word to change its meaning in some way. This change in meaning is usually small. For example, *art* could change to *artist,* or *free* could change to *freedom.* Sometimes, however, a suffix makes a big change. For example, adding *-less* to *hope* makes *hopeless,* which is very different.

Sometimes suffixes are added to whole words that you already know. You can often figure out the meaning of an unfamiliar word if you see that it contains a suffix.

This table shows some common suffixes and their meanings. Use this information to complete all of the exercises.

SUFFIX	MEANING	EXAMPLES
ant, ent	one who; likely to	resident, servant
fy, ify	to make, form into, or become	beautify, justify
ty, ity	quality, state, or condition	specialty, purity
ive	having the quality of; tending to	active, productive
ize	to cause to be, become, or make	alphabetize, fertilize
ous	full of or having qualities of	courageous, joyous

Exercise A

These are common words that contain suffixes. Write the suffix on the line next to each word.

1. glorify _____

2. humanity _____

3. marvelous _____

4. contestant _____

5. creative _____

6. personify _____

7. appreciative _____

8. dangerous _____

9. familiarity _____

10. occupant _____

Exercise B

Write the letter of the word or phrase that means the same thing as each word on the left.

_____ 11. simplify   A. hidden

_____ 12. secretive   B. cruelty

_____ 13. elasticity   C. destructive

_____ 14. brutality   D. make easy

_____ 15. ruinous   E. stretchiness

Exercise C

Use what you know about the base words and suffixes to answer the questions.

____ 16. If your behavior is *imitative,* what might you be called?
   A. a copycat   B. a chicken   C. a bully

____ 17. What causes water to *solidify?*
   A. boiling it   B. freezing it   C. stirring it

____ 18. What do people who like to *socialize* probably enjoy?
   A. parties   B. reading   C. driving

____ 19. What word describes someone who is often *insistent?*
   A. weak   B. unlucky   C. stubborn

____ 20. Where would a person be likely to go as a result of his or her *criminality?*
   A. to bed   B. to school   C. to jail

Exercise D

Combine the suffix and the word that is shown to make a new word. Then write a sentence that uses the new word.

21. legal + ize   _____

_____

_____

22. combat + ant   _____

_____

_____

23. odor + ous   _____

_____

_____

24. rapid + ity   _____

_____

_____

25. express + ive   _____

_____

_____

Know-How

Homographs

A word may be spelled the same as another word but have a completely different meaning. These words are called **homographs**. (That means that they are written the same way.) Usually, only one of the meanings makes sense in the sentence or paragraph you're reading.

Exercise A
Circle the letter of the correct meaning for each underlined word.

1. I'm going to sit on the <u>bank</u> and fish this afternoon.
   A. land along a river
   B. building where money is kept

2. Our seats were <u>close</u> to the stage.
   A. shut
   B. near

3. When you get home, give me a <u>ring</u> and we'll talk about the homework.
   A. phone call
   B. jewelry for a finger

4. If you <u>lead</u>, I will follow.
   A. kind of metal
   B. show the way

Sometimes you will see a word that looks familiar but doesn't make sense with the meaning you know. For example, "The pants were made of *duck.*" Those might be very odd pants, but it's more likely that *duck* has a less familiar meaning. It does. A dictionary would show you that it can mean "a kind of cloth."

Exercise B
Each underlined word has several meanings. Write the word in each sentence that someone would most likely need to look up in a dictionary.

5. I do <u>well</u> when I <u>play</u> <u>ball</u> even though I have a <u>game</u> leg.

   _____

6. In the <u>light</u>, we <u>saw</u> that the barn had begun to <u>list</u> toward the <u>pen</u>.

   _____

7. There is a <u>minute</u> amount of <u>soil</u> <u>left</u>—only a <u>bit</u>, really.

   _____

8. Bread is a <u>staple</u>, so it is <u>rare</u> for a <u>home</u> to be without a <u>loaf</u> or two.

   _____

A dictionary can tell you what words mean. However, you still have to decide which of a word's meanings is the one you need to know. Look at these sample dictionary entries for what *shock* can mean as a noun.

shock¹ (shok) *noun* **1.** a sudden, strong blow, shake, or disturbance *[The shock of the crash crushed the car.]* **2.** a sudden, strong upsetting of the mind or feelings *[news that is a shock]* **3.** the effect on the body of an electric current *[That wire could give you a shock.]* **4.** *in Medicine:* a physical problem caused by serious injury, pain, or loss of blood *[suffering from shock]*

shock² (shok) *noun* a group of stalks of grain or corn, stacked together to dry *[near a shock of corn]*

shock³ (shok) *noun* a bushy, thick mass, as of hair *[her shock of curls]*

Exercise C

Write the letter that matches the meaning *shock* has in each sentence.

A. **shock¹**, definition 1
B. **shock¹**, definition 2
C. **shock¹**, definition 3
D. **shock¹**, definition 4
E. **shock²**
F. **shock³**

____ 9. The price of the new car was a *shock*.

____ 10. Sticking a fork in a toaster can give you a terrible *shock*.

____ 11. A barber could take care of that shaggy *shock* of yours.

____ 12. The earthquake's second *shock* was milder than the first.

____ 13. While we're in the field, if you hold each *shock* together, I'll tie it.

____ 14. He's very pale, and his heartbeat is rapid; I think he's in *shock*.

____ 15. The *shock* of the wave knocked me right off my feet.

Know-How

Using What You Know

There are many ways to figure out what a word means. You can, of course, look it up in a dictionary. You can ask someone who is familiar with the word. Another way that often works is to use what you already know.

Here's a hard word: *disjoined*. Most people don't know what this word means until they're almost through with high school. But it's really easy to figure out.

Example: *disjoined = dis + joined*

joined means "put together"

dislike means "not like"

disjoined means "not put together"

Words you know can often help you figure out words you don't know. When you see an unfamiliar word, ask yourself if it has any familiar parts. If it does, go from there.

Exercise A

For each "hard" word, write the base word. Think about it and about a familiar word. Then use what you know to answer each question.

1. misdeed　　　_____

   Think about *misfortune*. What might *misdeed* mean?

   _____

2. appointee　　_____

   Think about *employee*. What might an *appointee* be?

   _____

3. climatic　　　_____

   Think about *acrobatic*. What is an example of a *climatic* event?

   _____

4. tricolored　　_____

   Think about *tricycle*. What might *tricolored* mean?

   _____

A hard word isn't always long. And you can't always break it up into familiar parts. But you still may be able to get a lot of help from words you already know.

Exercise B

Use what you know about the underlined word to figure out what the word in italics means. Write the letter of the answer on the line.

_____ 5. By thinking about <u>flexible</u>, you can tell that to *flex* something is to
    A. bend it.   B. break it.   C. create it.

_____ 6. By thinking about <u>pretend</u>, you can tell that a *pretense* of friendship is
    A. deep.   B. not real.   C. funny.

_____ 7. By thinking about <u>after</u> and <u>effect</u>, you can tell that an *aftereffect* is a
    A. surprise.   B. decoration.   C. later result.

_____ 8. By thinking about <u>habit</u>, you can tell that someone who is *habitually* late is
    A. never late.   B. sometimes late.   C. almost always late.

_____ 9. By thinking about <u>profit</u>, you can tell that a *profiteer's* main interest is
    A. shopping.   B. making money.   C. helping others.

_____ 10. By thinking about <u>break</u> and <u>neck</u>, you can tell that a *breakneck* action is
    A. dangerous.   B. illegal.   C. amusing.

_____ 11. By thinking about <u>system</u>, you can tell that a *systematic* way of doing things is
    A. sloppy.   B. quick.   C. well planned.

_____ 12. By thinking about <u>blabbermouth</u>, you can tell that a person who is *blabbing* is
    A. laughing.   B. talking.   C. acting strangely.

Know-How

The **context** of a word is the phrase, sentence, or paragraph in which it appears. A word's context always supplies some clue or clues to its meaning. Sometimes those clues may not be much help, but sometimes they are very helpful.

For example:

He's a *curmudgeon*!
Curmudgeon is a noun.

I don't want to act like a *curmudgeon*.
Curmudgeon is a noun and probably not something good.

Her bad temper, rudeness, and grumpiness soon gave her a reputation as a *curmudgeon*.
Curmudgeon is a noun that means someone who has a bad temper and is rude and grumpy.

The last example for *curmudgeon* actually provides a definition of the word. This occurs sometimes, but a reader usually doesn't get that much help.

A common kind of context clue is one that provides a word that means the same, or almost the same, thing.

For example:

I felt *peckish,* and there were reasons for me to be so irritable.
This suggests that *peckish* and *irritable* are similar in meaning.

Of course I *denounce* that action! Who wouldn't disapprove?
It is clear that someone who denounces something disapproves of it.

Another useful kind of context clue tells you that something is the opposite of something else, or at least quite different.

For example:

Unlike Matt, who was cowardly, Terry was *plucky*.
Plucky means something quite different than *cowardly*.

Some of my problems were important, but some *were piddling*.
Piddling means something quite different than *important*.

Another way that context clues can help is by giving one or more examples.

For example:

My *mishaps* included twisting my ankle, dropping my homework in the snow, and losing my keys.
These events are all mishaps, so a mishap is probably some sort of unlucky accident.

Frank didn't have a car, so his *conveyance* was usually a bicycle.
"Car" and "bicycle" appear to be examples of conveyances, so a conveyance is probably a vehicle.

Although context clues rarely tell you exactly what a word means, they do often give you an idea about its meaning.

Exercise

Use context clues to get an idea of what the underlined word means. Write the letter of the word's likely meaning on the line.

____ 1. We sat down and dug in to a <u>repast</u> of chicken, potatoes, corn, salad, and rolls.
    A. rest   C. memory
    B. meal   D. conversation

____ 2. I can't help you if you just sigh and groan. Can you <u>verbalize</u> what the problem is? If you tell me about it, maybe I can help.
    A. say   C. imagine
    B. notice   D. ignore

____ 3. The mother and father robin both carried food to the <u>fledglings</u> in the nest.
    A. sticks   C. enemies
    B. feathers   D. young birds

____ 4. Barry drove a flashy sports car, wore a diamond ring on his little finger, and gave hundred-dollar tips. He loved to <u>flaunt</u> his wealth.
    A. discuss   C. ignore
    B. show off   D. increase

____ 5. We expected Jeff to be happy when we told him the news. Instead, it made him <u>melancholy</u>.
    A. surprised   C. sad
    B. dangerous   D. famous

____ 6. Whether it is a cabin, a mansion, a straw hut, or a high-rise apartment, each person's <u>domicile</u> should be a place of safety.
    A. family   C. home
    B. school   D. country

____ 7. History is not just about kings and queens, presidents, generals, popes, and other such <u>personages</u>. It should also tell the stories of the common people.
    A. men   C. odd characters
    B. events   D. important people

____ 8. Lila shook her head in an <u>obdurate</u> way, just as hardheaded as usual.
    A. stubborn   C. intelligent
    B. agreeable   D. mysterious

Know-How

An **analogy** is a way of comparing things that have similar relationships. Here's an example.

A <u>kitten</u> is a baby <u>cat</u>, just as a <u>puppy</u> is a baby <u>dog</u>.

Exercise A

Fill in the blank with a word that completes each analogy.

1. A <u>girl</u> grows up to be a <u>woman</u>, just as a <u>boy</u> grows up to be a _____

2. The foot of a <u>dog</u> is called a <u>paw</u>, just as the foot of a <u>horse</u> is called a _____

3. A <u>pound</u> is a measure of <u>weight</u>, just as a <u>mile</u> is a measure of _____

4. A group of <u>wolves</u> is called a <u>pack</u>, just as a group of <u>cows</u> is called a _____

5. <u>Up</u> is the opposite of <u>down</u>, just as <u>in</u> is the opposite of _____

Those analogies tell how the pairs of things go together. They explain the relationship. Analogies on worksheets and tests don't give all this information. Instead, they usually look like this:

swamp : wet :: desert : ?

To complete an analogy like this, you have to figure out how the first two words go together. Make up a sentence that describes the relationship. "A <u>swamp</u> is a place that is <u>wet</u>." Then, think about how to finish the analogy. "A <u>desert</u> is a place that is . . . <u>dry</u>."

Examples: *mitten : hand*   A <u>mitten</u> is worn on a <u>hand</u>.

sad : happy   <u>Sad</u> is the opposite of <u>happy</u>.

cow : grass   A <u>cow</u> eats <u>grass</u>.

oven : bake   An <u>oven</u> is used to <u>bake</u> things.

Exercise B

Write a short sentence that describes the relationship between each pair of words. This exercise continues on the next page.

6. *apple : fruit* _____

_____

7. *happy : glad* _____

_____

8. *eyes : see* _____

_____

9. *hammer : pound* _____

_____

10. *boat : water* _____

_____

Figuring out the relationship between the first two words is the first step. Then you must find another pair of words that go together the same way. You can do this by putting the new words in the sentence you made up and seeing which ones make sense.

Example: *chapter : book :: day :*
            A. night   C. week
            B. diary   D. sunrise

Step 1:   A <u>chapter</u> is part of a <u>book</u>.

Step 2:   A. A <u>day</u> is part of a <u>night</u>.
            B. A <u>day</u> is part of a <u>diary</u>.
            C. A <u>day</u> is part of a <u>week</u>.
            D. A <u>day</u> is part of a <u>sunrise</u>.

Step 3:   Answer C is the only one that makes a sensible sentence.

Exercise C

Choose the word that completes each analogy. Write the letter on the line.

____ 11. *apple : fruit :: carrot :*
         A. orange   C. salad
         B. rabbit   D. vegetable

____ 12. *happy : glad :: big :*
         A. size   C. large
         B. small   D. strong

____ 13. *eyes : see :: ears :*
         A. hear   C. head
         B. sound   D. earring

____ 14. *hammer : pound :: scissors :*
         A. cut   C. sew
         B. sharp   D. paper

____ 15. *boat : water :: car :*
         A. tire   C. roads
         B. truck   D. gasoline

Know-How

Analogies 2

There are many kinds of relationships that are used in analogies. Here are some common kinds.

		Examples
A.	Synonyms	*harm : damage :: guard : protect*
B.	Antonyms	*love : hate :: soothe : upset*
C.	Part to Whole	*violin : orchestra :: singer : choir*
D.	Worker and Tool	*carpenter : hammer :: painter : brush*
E.	Characteristic	*fire : hot :: ice : cold*
F.	Object and Purpose	*saw : cut :: shovel : dig*
G.	Example	*trout : fish :: lion : cat*
H.	Manner	*nibble : eat :: sip : drink*
I.	Degree or Intensity	*warm : hot :: cool : cold*

Exercise A

Decide which type of relationship each word pair involves. Write the letter (from the list above) on the line.

_____ 1. *farmer : plow*

_____ 2. *mule : stubborn*

_____ 3. *canoe : boat*

_____ 4. *tired : exhausted*

_____ 5. *rough : smooth*

_____ 6. *soap : clean*

_____ 7. *sofa : couch*

_____ 8. *letter : alphabet*

Sometimes, the first two words in an analogy can go together in several ways. You may have to guess about the right way to explain their relationship. You know your guess is right if only one answer choice works. What should you do if more than one answer works?

Example: *attractive : beautiful :: afraid :*
          A. sorry   C. fearless
          B. scared   D. terrified

Sentence: <u>Attractive</u> is a synonym for <u>beautiful</u>.

Result: Two answers are correct:
          <u>Afraid</u> is a synonym for <u>scared</u>.
          <u>Afraid</u> is a synonym for <u>terrified</u>.

Only one answer can be the correct one. So what should you do? The solution is to explain the relationship between the first two words more exactly.

Sentence: Someone who is extremely <u>attractive</u> is <u>beautiful</u>.

Result: Now, only one answer is correct:
          Someone who is extremely <u>afraid</u> is <u>terrified</u>.

Exercise B

Choose the word that completes each analogy. Write the letter on the line.

_____ 9. *sun : day :: moon :*
    A. sky   C. light
    B. stars   D. night

_____ 10. *arm : elbow :: leg :*
    A. knee   C. foot
    B. thigh   D. ankle

_____ 11. *oak : tree :: rose :*
    A. thorn   C. flower
    B. scent   D. garden

_____ 12. *broom : sweep :: pencil :*
    A. paper   C. erase
    B. write   D. sharpen

Some analogies require you to choose the whole second pair. You should work this kind the same way, by figuring out how the first pair goes together.

Example: *bird : feathers ::*
    A. fish : lake   C. rabbit : fur
    B. bee : honey   D. horse : gallop

Answer: The description could be "A bird has feathers" or "A bird is covered with feathers." Either way, the only pair that has the same relationship is C.

Exercise C

Decide which pair of words completes each analogy. Write the letter on the line.

_____ 13. *teacher : classroom ::*
    A. artist : painting   C. secretary : office
    B. piano : music   D. student : homework

_____ 14. *racket : tennis ::*
    A. bat : baseball   C. game : sport
    B. coach : athlete   D. throw : catch

_____ 15. *feather : light ::*
    A. wren : bird   C. person : smart
    B. steel : hard   D. snack : healthy

Lesson 1

aggravate *AG•ruh•vate* VERB

1. to irritate or annoy [Don't *aggravate* me by interrupting.]

2. to make worse [Scratching your rash will only *aggravate* the condition.]

comprehend *kom•pree•HEND* VERB

to understand fully [Do you *comprehend* my instructions?]

cower *KOW•ur* VERB

to crouch and tremble; to shrink back in fear or because of pain [Whenever the cruel king was angry, all his servants would *cower*.]

endure *en•DUR* VERB

1. to last; to continue to exist [Did your house *endure* the earthquake?]

2. to put up with or bear; to show lasting strength [I don't think I can *endure* any more complaints.]

frugal *FROO•gul* ADJECTIVE

thrifty; not wasteful [My *frugal* parents often serve leftovers.]

futile *FYOO•tul* ADJECTIVE

useless, worthless, or hopeless; not effective [Our efforts to put out the fire were *futile*.]

immense *ih•MENCE* ADJECTIVE

huge; enormous [Blue whales are *immense* creatures.]

insufficient *in•suh•FISH•unt* ADJECTIVE

not as much as is needed [A light jacket is *insufficient* on a freezing day.]

laborious *luh•BOR•ee•us* ADJECTIVE

involving or requiring labor or much hard work; difficult [Plowing rocky soil is a *laborious* job.]

malice *MAL•us* NOUN

the desire to harm another; ill will [It is reasonable to fear someone who shows *malice* toward you.]

parasite *PAIR•uh•site* NOUN

1. a plant or animal that lives on (or within) another from which it gets food [A flea is a *parasite*.]

2. one who lives at another's expense without contributing anything of value [Uncle Ed is a *parasite* who expects Grandma to support him.]

predicament *pree•DIK•uh•munt* NOUN

a difficult or unpleasant situation [Our flat tire put us in a *predicament*.]

scoff *SKOF* VERB

to show scorn; to look down on or make fun of someone or something [People used to *scoff* at early automobiles, but that attitude didn't last.]

trivial *TRIV•ee•ul* ADJECTIVE

not valuable or important [Let's not argue about *trivial* things.]

unanimous *yoo•NAN•uh•mus* ADJECTIVE

in (or based on) complete agreement [The group's decision was *unanimous*.]

Alice   Malice

Exercise A: Synonyms

Write the Word that best completes each sentence.

1. If you are "up a creek without a paddle," you're in a ___.   _____

2. Someone who believes in "waste not, want not" is ___.   _____

3. If you make a situation "go from bad to worse." you ___ it.   _____

4. Something that is "big as a house" or "jumbo" is ___.   _____

5. A task that is an "uphill battle" or "easier said than done" is ___.   _____

6. When a group of people "see eye to eye," their decision is ___.   _____

7. If you "get it," "catch on," or "see the light," you ___ it.   _____

8. If you "poke fun" at something or "look down your nose," you ___.   _____

9. If you "hang in there" and "stick it out," you will ___.   _____

10. If something is "no big deal" or "makes no difference," it is ___.   _____

Exercise B: Other Forms of Words

Use what you know about the Words to choose the correct answers.

____ 11. If a team **unanimously** decides to buy new uniforms, how many people vote no?
    A. none   B. only a few   C. almost half

____ 12. Which kind of track event requires the most **endurance**?
    A. high jump   B. 2-mile race   C. 50-meter sprint

____ 13. Which words would probably be spoken by a **cowering** person?
    A. "Oh, yeah?"   B. "I can't wait!"   C. "Don't hurt me!"

____ 14. Who are most likely to behave **maliciously** toward each other?
    A. friends   B. enemies   C. co-workers

____ 15. If you are **insufficiently** fed, how do you feel?
    A. stuffed   B. hungry   C. comfortable

____ 16. What would you be most likely to think of as an **aggravation**?
    A. a constant itch   B. a burning house   C. a birthday cake

____ 17. Which of these things is supposed to measure **comprehension**?
    A. a yardstick   B. a bathroom scale   C. a classroom test

Question: What do you call a rude flea?

Answer: An impolite parasite

Exercise C: Questions
Write the Word that best answers the question.

18. What does the saying "A penny saved is a penny earned" encourage people to be?

_____

19. What are you in when your boat springs a leak a long way from shore?

_____

20. What do the two sides involved in a feud usually feel toward each other?

_____

21. If a big dog starts growling and snapping at a puppy, what is the puppy likely to do?

_____

22. When a teacher explains something, what does he or she hope the students will do?

_____

23. What kind of creature is a tick (or a person who behaves like one)?

_____

24. If you got a sunburn, what kind of protection did you get from your sunscreen lotion?

_____

25. What kind of job would it be to scrub the kitchen floor on your hands and knees?

_____

Exercise D: Antonyms
Write the Word that is an antonym for each word.

26. effective _____

27. easy _____

28. admire _____

29. collapse _____

30. provider _____

31. enough _____

32. important _____

33. soothe _____

34. wasteful _____

35. tiny _____

Exercise E: Writing
An "exercise in *futility*" is an effort that just won't succeed, no matter what! It could be asking a bully to "play nice" or trying to patch a leaky roof with Scotch tape. On your own paper, describe what you think would be a **futile** effort, or an exercise in futility. Use THREE Words in your description.

There are days when home-work seems laborious and trying to concentrate is an exercise in futility.

Quick LIST

aggravate V.	**endure** V.	**immense** ADJ.	**malice** N.	**scoff** V.
comprehend V.	**frugal** ADJ.	**insufficient** ADJ.	**parasite** N.	**trivial** ADJ.
cower V.	**futile** ADJ.	**laborious** ADJ.	**predicament** N.	**unanimous** ADJ.

Exercise F: Fill-in

Write the Word that best completes each sentence. Use each word only once.

36. Lily talked awhile about _____ matters before telling her friend the big news.

37. Robbie is not a _____; he always does his fair share of work around the house.

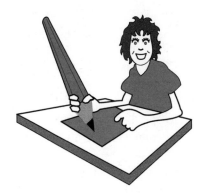

Alice with an immense pencil

38. The crowd at the championship game was _____ and filled the gymnasium.

39. I can't _____ anything my neighbors say because they speak German and I don't.

40. Tina's parents were _____ for many years so that they could send her to college.

41. If my family had to plan a vacation based on a _____ decision, we would never go anywhere!

42. I don't mind setting the table, but I hate _____ jobs like scrubbing the kitchen floor.

43. It's unkind to _____ at people who are doing the best they can.

A guy with an insufficient supply of hair

44. It was a feeling of _____ that made someone put a big scratch on our car with a key.

45. Farmers face hardships when there is _____ rain during the growing season.

46. Ben made many _____ attempts to make his stubborn horse trot.

47. Mia was in a _____ when she locked herself out of the house on a freezing cold day.

48. I thought that making noise might _____ my mother's headaches, so I tried to keep quiet.

49. A child who is not used to horses might _____ when one approaches, even if it's friendly.

50. The ability of the United States to _____ was in doubt during the Civil War.

A super guy who never cowers

Lesson 2

cliché *klee•SHAY* NOUN

a phrase that is no longer very effective or meaningful because of being used too often ["Busy as a bee" is a *cliché*.]

commend *kuh•MEND* VERB

to speak of with approval; to praise [I want to *commend* you for your bravery.]

competent *KOM•puh•tent* ADJECTIVE

able to do something [Greg is quite *competent* in the kitchen, so the dinner he made for us was delicious.]

deception *dih•SEP•shun* NOUN

a trick or lie; something that deceives [A scarecrow is a *deception* that makes crows think a person is in the field.]

drudgery *DRUJ•ur•ee* NOUN

dull, uninteresting work [Scrubbing floors is *drudgery*.]

erode *ee•RODE* VERB

to wear away slowly [Rains began to *erode* the river bank.]

falter *FOL•tur* VERB

1. to hesitate; to not go straight onward; to lose courage [The soldiers did not *falter* even though they faced almost certain death.]

2. to speak in a hesitating way; to stammer [If you don't know the answer, you may *falter* when you try to give it.]

hoard *HORD*

NOUN a stored supply, often hidden [The squirrel has a *hoard* of nuts.]

VERB to store up for future use; to collect, often in a greedy way [We began to *hoard* food supplies when we heard that a big snowstorm was coming.]

intimidate *in•TIM•uh•date* VERB

to frighten; to influence by fear [No bully is going to *intimidate* me!]

"This is Mary Sue Moss. Today we'll be talking to folks who have messages for Cinderella. What do you have to say, Mr. Stein?"

"Nnnn. Wicked old stepmother not intimidate Frankie."

jubilant *JOO•buh•lunt* ADJECTIVE

feeling great joy; filled with gladness and rejoicing; happy enough to shout [We were all *jubilant* when Ronna scored the winning run.]

luscious *LUSH•us* ADJECTIVE

delicious; extremely sweet and pleasing to any of the senses [The fresh peaches made a *luscious* pie.]

offend *uh•FEND* VERB

to cause [someone] to feel hurt or angry; to insult [I don't want to *offend* you, but you do look silly in that hat.]

retrieve *rih•TREEV* VERB

to get back; to recover [I dropped a quarter in the snow but was able to *retrieve* it.]

steadfast *STED•fast* ADJECTIVE

1. firm and unchanging [Lincoln's *steadfast* belief was that the Union should be preserved.]

2. loyal; true [Helen and I have been *steadfast* friends for many years.]

tact *TAKT* NOUN

the ability to deal with difficult situations without making people feel hurt or insulted [It requires *tact* to tell a friend you're voting for someone else for class president.]

Exercise A: Story Time

Write the Word that best completes each sentence. Use each word only once.

Before she met the prince, Cinderella's young life was filled with **[1]**. It is a **[2]** to say that she worked her fingers to the bone, but it is true. Although she wanted to go to the ball, her stepmother bullied and threatened and managed to **[3]** her into staying at home alone.

However, Cinderella's fairy godmother gave her beautiful clothes and a coach. Cinderella felt **[4]**! She met the prince, who was quite a **[5]** dancer, and they glided happily across the floor for hours. Cinderella didn't want to **[6]** the prince by running away suddenly without any explanation, but she had to when she heard the clock begin to strike twelve. Hearing that sound, she did not **[7]**, but instead ran quickly to the coach. One slipper came off, and she didn't have time to go back to **[8]** it.

The prince was **[9]** in his love for Cinderella, and he searched the entire kingdom, looking for the woman whose foot fit the lost slipper. Each of Cinderella's stepsisters pretended the slipper was hers, but this **[10]** did not work because the slipper did not fit. The king's assistants found other ladies to **[11]**, but the prince didn't care how lovely or nice they were; he loved only Cinderella. Nothing could **[12]** his faith that he would find her and, when he did, they lived happily ever after.

1. _____

2. _____

3. _____

4. _____

5. _____

6. _____

7. _____

8. _____

9. _____

10. _____

11. _____

12. _____

Exercise B: Other Forms of Words

Use what you know about the Words to choose the correct answers.

_____ 13. Which is an example of **commendable** behavior?
  A. cheating B. truthfulness C. laughing

_____ 14. Farms are most likely to suffer from **erosion** as a result of what?
  A. floods B. insects C. cold weather

_____ 15. What kind of clothing is meant to be **deceptive**?
  A. a uniform B. a disguise C. an evening gown

_____ 16. What might a person say **jubilantly**?
  A. "Hurray!" B. "Rats!" C. "Keep trying."

_____ 17. What do **tactful** people try not to hurt?
  A. themselves B. the Earth C. others' feelings

"My name is Osgood, and I think Cinderella is just luscious."

"Stories about weak, silly women offend me! And so does that twerp Osgood!"

Exercise C: True or False

Circle TRUE or FALSE for each statement.

18. A miser is someone who **hoards** his or her money. . . . . TRUE   FALSE

19. Most people would consider a picnic on the beach to be **drudgery**. . . . . TRUE   FALSE

20. If you know exactly what to say, you are likely to **falter** when you say it. . . . . . . TRUE   FALSE

21. People who express themselves in original ways use many **clichés**. . . . . TRUE   FALSE

22. Telling an umpire he's blind as a bat would probably **offend** him. . . . . TRUE   FALSE

23. Dessert is supposed to be a **luscious** part of a meal. . . . . TRUE   FALSE

Exercise D: Antonyms

Write the Word that is an antonym for each set of words.

24. lose; misplace

25. blame; criticize

26. build up; add to

27. unskillful; not able

28. flatter; praise; please

29. share; use up; distribute

30. encourage; inspire; reassure

31. sad; sorrowful; disappointed

32. changeable; temporary; weak

33. truthfulness; honesty; sincerity

34. clumsy comments; thoughtlessness

35. disgusting; nasty-tasting; unpleasing

"Oh, I'm on? Er, yes, I'm, uh, Bob, and I think the prince is very competent, for a, um, er, prince. . . . Did I falter too much?"

"I woulda fetched yer shlipper, but ya didn't ashk. Ya want me to retrieve shomethin now? Huh? Do ya? I will."

Quick LIST

cliché N.	**deception** N.	**falter** V.	**jubilant** ADJ.	**retrieve** V.
commend V.	**drudgery** N.	**hoard** N., V.	**luscious** ADJ.	**steadfast** ADJ.
competent ADJ.	**erode** V.	**intimidate** V.	**offend** V.	**tact** N.

Exercise E: Fill-in

Write the Word that best completes each sentence. Use each word only once.

36. I hate copying a paper over; it's such _____.

37. Every game that I lost helped to _____ my confidence just a little more.

38. As a _____ to draw a fox away from her nest, a bird might pretend her wing is broken.

39. You have to be a _____ carpenter to build a sturdy house.

40. It is selfish to _____ supplies just for yourself when everyone needs them.

41. Pears are never more _____ than they are at this time of year.

42. Georgia was _____ when she found out she had won the contest.

43. Yoshi ran back into the school to _____ his forgotten backpack.

44. It would have shown _____ to say "I think you can do better" instead of "Gosh, that was horrible!"

45. A strange noise made me _____ as I started to go into the dark basement.

46. If we let the other team _____ us, we won't have the confidence we need to play well.

47. Jenny's teachers _____ her for trying even though she doesn't always get A's.

48. Ted never gives up because he has the _____ belief that he will someday succeed.

49. You will probably _____ the person who gave you a gift if you just toss it aside after opening it.

50. It is often easier to use a _____ than to think of a fresh, new way to say something.

"Happily ever after? That's a cliché. Excuse my lack of tact."

"Drudgery? You think you had drudgery? Ha! Honey, I'll show you drudgery!"

"I am jubilant to see that your love has remained steadfast. Cheers!"

"*My dear girl*, I do hope our tiny misunderstanding will not erode our relationship. Please do call soon, my darling. Your stepsisters and I miss you terribly."

Lesson 3

abhor *ab•HOR* VERB
to hate; to shrink from with disgust [I used to *abhor* spinach, but now I like it.]

acute *uh•KYOOT* ADJECTIVE
1. sharp and severe [I felt an *acute* pain in my side.]
2. keen or sensitive [Hawks have *acute* vision.]
3. very serious [There is an *acute* shortage of water.]

bicker *BIK•ur* VERB
to argue over an unimportant matter [Let's not *bicker* about who's taller.]

etiquette *ET•uh•kit* NOUN
the manners and behavior considered to be acceptable [Dining *etiquette* is different at a picnic than at a formal dinner.]

foolhardy *FOOL•har•dee* ADJECTIVE
foolishly daring [Jumping off the roof was a *foolhardy* act.]

genial *JEEN•yul* ADJECTIVE
pleasantly cheerful and kindly [It's a pleasure to have such *genial* neighbors.]

imply *im•PLY* VERB
to suggest or express without directly saying [I yawned to *imply* that I was bored.]

initiative *ih•NISH•uh•tiv* NOUN
1. the ability to see what needs to be done and take a leading role in getting it done [Her *initiative* makes her a natural leader.]
2. a first step or movement; an act that begins something [I took the *initiative* by introducing myself to the new student.]

menace *MEN•us*
NOUN a serious threat [Wolves can be a *menace* to sheep.]
VERB to threaten [A mother bear will *menace* anyone who gets near her cubs.]

persevere *pur•suh•VEER* VERB
to keep at something even though it is difficult [Success comes to those who *persevere*.]

ponder *PON•dur* VERB
to consider carefully; to think deeply about, often over a period of time [I need to *ponder* this decision.]

quaint *KWAYNT* ADJECTIVE
strange, odd, or old-fashioned in a pleasing way [She had a *quaint* bed that folded up into the wall.]

remorse *rih•MORCE* NOUN
deep regret and a feeling of guilt over one's wrongdoing [The boy showed *remorse* when he realized he'd hurt my feelings.]

vague *VAYG* ADJECTIVE
1. not clear or definite [Not knowing whether I actually wanted to attend the party, I gave a *vague* answer.]
2. fuzzy or blurred [The house was a *vague* shape in the darkness.]

vital *VY•tul* ADJECTIVE
very important; absolutely necessary [Using seatbelts is *vital* for safety.]

A genial girl

Exercise A: Completion
Choose the correct answer to complete each sentence.

_____ 1. A *vague* answer to your question is most likely to leave you feeling
    A. insulted.   B. satisfied.   C. confused.

_____ 2. An example of a *quaint* way to travel would be to use a
    A. skateboard.   B. horse and buggy.   C. helicopter.

_____ 3. A dog might *menace* someone by
    A. growling.   B. wagging its tail.   C. begging for food.

_____ 4. If you have questions about *etiquette*, you want to know how to
    A. behave.   B. make money.   C. keep house.

_____ 5. Someone who *perseveres* shows
    A. laziness.   B. determination.   C. kindness.

_____ 6. Something that most people would describe as *vital* is
    A. food.   B. perfume.   C. jokes.

Exercise B: Synonyms
Write the Word that is closest in meaning to each set of words and phrases.

7. manners; social rules; politeness   _____

8. continue; try, try again; last   _____

9. hint; indicate; mean   _____

10. drive; hustle; get-up-and-go   _____

11. friendly; easy-going; nice   _____

12. danger; peril; risk   _____

13. sorrow; an attack of conscience   _____

14. concentrate; study; keep in mind   _____

15. hazy; dim; uncertain   _____

16. quarrel; disagree; squabble   _____

A menace

Exercise C: True or False

Circle TRUE or FALSE for each statement.

17. In order to **imply** that something is untrue, you might say, "What a lie!" . . . . . .   TRUE   FALSE

18. If you make a **vague** request, people know exactly what you want. . . . .   TRUE   FALSE

19. You are most likely to **bicker** with people when you feel grouchy. . . . .   TRUE   FALSE

20. If your carelessness hurt a puppy, you'd probably feel **remorse**. . . . .   TRUE   FALSE

21. If you **ponder** a problem, you make up your mind right away. . . . .   TRUE   FALSE

22. People who **abhor** rock music play it as often as possible. . . . .   TRUE   FALSE

23. Shy people usually show **initiative** in making friends. . . . .   TRUE   FALSE

24. If something is **vital** to you, you can't do without it. . . . .   TRUE   FALSE

Exercise D: Analogies

Write the letter of the word that completes each analogy.

____ 25. *apologize :* **remorse** *:: laugh :*
   A. pride   B. sadness   C. gratitude   D. amusement

____ 26. *reckless :* **foolhardy** *:: brave :*
   A. careful   B. foolish   C. powerful   D. courageous

____ 27. *dislike :* **abhor** *:: like :*
   A. love   B. hate   C. enjoy   D. recommend

____ 28. **acute** *: mild :: quick :*
   A. first   B. slow   C. speedy   D. pointed

Exercise E: Antonyms

Write the Word that is an antonym for each of these words.

29. unimportant   _____

30. quit   _____

31. cautious   _____

32. adore   _____

33. unfriendly   _____

34. ordinary   _____

35. dull   _____

The menace
in a quaint disguise

Exercise F: Fill-in

Write the **Word** that best completes each sentence. Use each word only once.

Quick LIST

abhor V.
acute ADJ.
bicker V.
etiquette N.
foolhardy ADJ.
genial ADJ.
imply V.
initiative N.
menace N., V.
persevere V.
ponder V.
quaint ADJ.
remorse N.
vague ADJ.
vital ADJ.

36. Pioneer travelers had to _____ to make it all the way to California from the East.

37. My uncle greeted me at the door with a _____ smile that made me feel welcome.

38. Taking time to _____ a situation is the opposite of making a snap decision.

39. Every child should have the basic lessons in _____ of learning to say "please" and "thank you."

40. Mom gets angry when my brother and I _____ about who should set the table.

41. Victims with the most _____ injuries were treated first by the medical team.

42. A speeding car is a _____ to the safety of its passengers and other travelers.

43. Barb's _____ seemed sincere, so I forgave her for what she had done.

44. Eating healthy food is _____ to the development of bones and muscle.

45. Don't go fishing if you _____ handling worms.

46. We stayed at a _____ hotel that had feather beds covered with beautiful handmade quilts.

47. Lee is finally starting to show some _____; he used to do only as he was told.

48. To _____ that I should turn off the TV, my Dad said, "Why don't you get some exercise?"

49. Rita's _____ plan was to walk across the newly frozen pond.

50. Joe has only a _____ memory of Boston

The genial girl
in acute danger
from the menace
in a quaint disguise

Lesson 4

abrupt *uh•BRUPT* ADJECTIVE

happening suddenly or unexpectedly [The car came to an *abrupt* stop.]

acknowledge *ak•NOL•ij* VERB

1. to admit; to openly accept the truth of a fact [When you are wrong, it may be hard to *acknowledge* it.]

2. to recognize and answer [He sent a note to *acknowledge* my gift.]

adorn *uh•DORN* VERB

to add beauty to [Our neighbor likes to *adorn* her poodle with little pink bows.]

defiance *dih•FY•unce* NOUN

bold resistance; refusal to obey; an attitude or behavior that opposes someone or something powerful ["I won't, and you can't make me!" she said in *defiance*.]

dismal *DIZ•mul* ADJECTIVE

1. unpleasantly dim and gloomy [It was a *dismal*, rainy day.]

2. unhappy; cheerless [He responded to the bad news with a *dismal* sigh.]

folly *FOL•ee* NOUN

a lack of sense; foolishness; a foolish action or belief [It was *folly* for us to try to remove the beehive from the attic ourselves.]

illuminate *ih•LOO•mih•nate* VERB

to give light to [Turn on the lamp to *illuminate* the room.]

inevitable *in•EV•uh•tuh•bul* ADJECTIVE

certain to happen; unavoidable [When my brakes failed, I knew some sort of collision was *inevitable*.]

mere *MEER* ADJECTIVE

nothing more or other than; only [This wonderful toy cost a *mere* dollar.]

pamper *PAM•pur* VERB

to treat with too much gentleness; to give special care, privilege, and protection [His parents *pamper* him, so he's never learned to do anything on his own.]

Question:
What do you get from a pampered cow?

Answer:
Spoiled milk

perplex *pur•PLEX* VERB

to puzzle; to cause uncertainty and confusion [A mystery story may *perplex* a reader until the end.]

reverence *REV•ur•unce* NOUN

a feeling or attitude of deep respect [Our national anthem expresses a feeling of *reverence* for the flag.]

trounce *TROWNCE* VERB

to thoroughly beat or defeat [Our better players will *trounce* the other team.]

unique *yoo•NEEK* ADJECTIVE

1. so unusual as to have no like or equal [The design of each snowflake is *unique*.]

2. highly unusual or extremely rare [Tony's musical ability is *unique* in one so young.]

valor *VAL•ur* NOUN

great courage or bravery [The soldier received a medal for *valor*.]

Exercise A: Fill-in
Write the correct Word to complete each sentence.

Question:
What insect is always involved in folly?

Hint: Drop two letters. The answer drops in on another page.

1. My parents _____ me, at least a little, on my birthday.
   trounce   pamper   perplex

2. Identical twins look alike, but they are _____ individuals.
   mere   unique   abrupt

3. People use earrings, necklaces, and rings to _____ themselves.
   adorn   illuminate   acknowledge

4. People are often ashamed of behavior that was an act of _____.
   folly   valor   reverence

5. A professional ball team would probably _____ your school team.
   pamper   trounce   illuminate

6. If your key suddenly didn't work in your door, that would _____ you.
   trounce   perplex   illuminate

7. To emphasize how young a boy is, one might call him a _____ child.
   mere   dismal   unique

8. Sighing and groaning are ways that people show that they feel _____.
   dismal   abrupt   inevitable

9. You are refusing to _____ someone if you ignore a person who waves and calls to you.
   perplex   illuminate   acknowledge

10. A brat is likely to show _____ when told to do something he or she doesn't want to do.
   valor   defiance   reverence

Exercise B: Antonyms
Write the Word that is an antonym for each of these words.

11. wisdom _____
12. common _____
13. gradual _____
14. cheerful _____
15. deny _____

16. darken _____
17. unlikely _____
18. neglect _____
19. disrespect _____
20. cowardice _____

Exercise C: Completion

Choose the correct answer to complete each sentence.

____ 21. If you say you have a **mere** five dollars, you are suggesting that your money is
A. not enough.   B. plenty.   C. exactly the right amount.

____ 22. If you expect another team to **trounce** yours, you expect the other team to
A. play hard.   B. cheat.   C. win by a lot.

____ 23. An order would probably **perplex** you if it was given in
A. a rude way.   B. a cheerful voice.   C. a foreign language.

____ 24. Most people would describe as **folly** the effort to
A. get a job.   B. win a game.   C. turn iron into gold.

____ 25. An example of something that is **inevitable** is
A. a sunrise.   B. an accident.   C. a good test score.

____ 26. To **acknowledge** getting a letter, you could
A. save it.   B. write back.   C. read it carefully.

____ 27. The main reason to **adorn** something is to make it
A. safe.   B. easy to use.   C. more attractive.

____ 28. We expect judges to have a feeling of **reverence** toward
A. the law.   B. criminals.   C. jury members.

____ 29. One place that **pampers** people who go there is a
A. jail.   B. bus station.   C. luxury hotel.

____ 30. A person feeling **dismal** might say that he or she was
A. jumpy.   B. blue.   C. full of pep.

Exercise D: Other Forms of Words

Use what you know about the **Word** to choose the correct answers.

____ 31. A synonym for **adornments** is
A. *feelings.*   B. *decorations.*   C. *necessities.*

____ 32. One source of **illumination** is a
A. bed.   B. lamp.   C. playground.

____ 33. A job that often requires **valorous** behavior is that of
A. an artist.   B. a scientist.   C. a firefighter.

____ 34. A person who **defies** the law is a
A. criminal.   B. good citizen.   C. police officer.

____ 35. Something that happens **abruptly** is likely to occur
A. for no reason.   B. over and over.   C. with no warning.

Question:
How do you catch a
wild wabbit?

Answer:
Unique up on it.

Question:
How do you catch a
tame wabbit?

Answer:
The tame way!
Unique up on it!

A fly is always involved in *folly*. (Take away *ol*).

Exercise E: Fill-in

Write the Word that best completes each sentence. Use each word only once.

36. At night, a car needs headlights to _____ the road.

37. Don't expect perfect obedience from Rover; he's still a _____ puppy.

38. My little sister's plan to dig a tunnel to China is _____.

39. Adam demonstrated great _____ when he risked his own life to save me.

40. Jeff's style of painting is _____; I've never seen anything like it.

41. Bad directions and unclear maps _____ those who try to use them.

42. A feeling of _____ overcame me as I gazed at the memorial honoring those who had died to keep this nation free.

43. "You don't have to _____ me; I'm just as tough as anyone," said the old lady.

44. Lily is much faster than I am and is sure to _____ me in the race.

45. Getting older, like the changing of the seasons, is _____.

46. Barrettes and ribbons are often used to _____ hair.

47. The change was _____; one minute it was sunny, the next it was pouring rain.

48. We were punished for our _____ after we deliberately disobeyed the rules.

49. Some people won't _____ the fact that they're wrong, even when it's proven.

50. Our mood became as _____ as the weather when the game was canceled due to rain.

Question: What would you use to put a stop to folly?

Answer: A folly-swatter

Quick LIST

abrupt ADJ.	defiance N.	illuminate V.	pamper V.	trounce V.
acknowledge V.	dismal ADJ.	inevitable ADJ.	perplex V.	unique ADJ.
adorn V.	folly N.	mere ADJ.	reverence N.	valor N.

Lesson 5

abode uh•BODE NOUN

the place where one lives   [Ben's *abode* is a cabin by a lake.]

agitate AJ•uh•tate VERB

to excite or disturb   [She didn't want to *agitate* her grandmother with bad news.]

ample AM•pul ADJECTIVE

enough or more than enough   [We packed *ample* clothing for the trip.]

belittle bih•LIT•tul VERB

to make someone or something seem small or unimportant   [Joan tried to *belittle* the house by calling it a shack.]

Question:
How could you belittle an elephant?

Answer: You couldn't.
An elephant is just too big to be little!

clamor KLAM•ur

NOUN   a loud and continuing noise   [The parade's *clamor* could be heard blocks away.]

VERB   to cry out loudly; to make a loud and continuing noise   [The crowd began to *clamor* for the candidate to make an appearance.]

compassion kum•PASH•un NOUN

a feeling of sorrow or pity for another   [They showed their *compassion* for the homeless.]

fugitive FYOO•juh•tiv NOUN

a person who is running away, usually one trying to escape capture by the law   [The detectives followed the trail of the *fugitive*.]

linger LING•gur VERB

to continue to stay, usually because of being unwilling to leave   [It's nice to *linger* by the fire on a cold night.]

listless LIST•lus ADJECTIVE

showing no interest in what is going on; having no desire to do anything active   [She sighed in a *listless* way and went to bed.]

melancholy MEL•un•kol•ee ADJECTIVE

sad or gloomy   [Joe sang a *melancholy* tune.]

perceive pur•SEEV VERB

to see, hear, taste, smell, or feel; to be aware of   [Do you *perceive* the odor of something burning?]

perish PAIR•ish VERB

to be destroyed, ruined, or wiped out; to die   [If it doesn't rain soon, the crop will *perish*.]

relish REL•ish

NOUN   enjoyment; anything that adds pleasure or interest   [He ate with great *relish*.]

VERB   to like very much; to enjoy greatly   [I always *relish* a good science fiction story.]

reminisce rem•uh•NIS VERB

to think, talk, or write about one's experiences in the past   [My grandparents used the visit to *reminisce* about the old days.]

timidity tih•MID•uh•tee NOUN

a lack of courage or confidence; shyness   [Her *timidity* in a crowd was plain to see.]

Exercise A: Synonyms

Write the Word that could be used in place of each underlined word or phrase.

1. A police dog tracked the <u>runaway</u>. _____

2. A wolf's howl sounds so <u>sorrowful</u>! _____

3. We heard the <u>racket</u> of angry voices. _____

4. The news will <u>upset</u> the neighborhood. _____

5. This will surely be <u>plenty of</u> food for us. _____

6. We stayed at my aunt's <u>home</u> in Arizona. _____

7. People would <u>die</u> if they couldn't get food. _____

8. Let's look at these old photos and <u>remember</u>. _____

9. We'd better not <u>remain</u> here, or we'll be late. _____

10. Do you <u>notice</u> the smell of something burning? _____

Question:
What's green and makes a clamor?

Answer:
A froghorn

Exercise B: True or False

Circle TRUE or FALSE for each statement.

11. On a hot day, you would **relish** a cool swim. . . . .   TRUE   FALSE

12. Your ears can **perceive** the sound of an ant walking. . . . .   TRUE   FALSE

13. People feel proud and happy when you **belittle** them. . . . .   TRUE   FALSE

14. Adults **reminisce** when they tell stories about their childhoods. . . . . . .   TRUE   FALSE

15. A cotton shirt provides **ample** warmth for a freezing day. . . . .   TRUE   FALSE

16. You would be likely to **linger** at a place you enjoy. . . . .   TRUE   FALSE

17. If a bee scares you, you should try to **agitate** it. . . . .   TRUE   FALSE

18. One animal that often shows **timidity** is a lion. . . . . . .   TRUE   FALSE

19. Most people have mail sent to their **abodes**. . . . .   TRUE   FALSE

20. A **listless** person just can't calm down. . . . .   TRUE   FALSE

Question:
If you like your hot dog with everything, how do you eat it?

Answer: With relish (But you may feel listless about eating a blue one!)

Exercise C: Analogies

Write the letter of the word pair that completes the analogy.

____ 21. *clamor* : ears ::
   A. bird : song
   B. taste : food
   C. odor : nose
   D. weight : height

____ 22. *ample* : scarce ::
   A. plain : fancy
   B. tiny : small
   C. rare : expensive
   D. warm : hot

____ 23. whimper : *melancholy* ::
   A. shout : nervous
   B. sob : angry
   C. growl : scary
   D. laugh : amused

____ 24. *fugitive* : posse ::
   A. horse : saddle
   B. rabbit : hawk
   C. car : brakes
   D. nightmare : dream

____ 25. mansion : *abode* ::
   A. tree : flower
   B. nest : bird
   C. cabin : logs
   D. elephant : animal

Exercise D: Antonyms

Write the Word that is an antonym for each set of words.

26. overlook; fail to notice   _____

27. bravery; confidence   _____

28. soothe; calm down   _____

29. survive; last   _____

30. cruelty; meanness   _____

31. cheerful; happy   _____

32. energetic; enthusiastic   _____

33. leave; depart   _____

34. flatter; honor; exaggerate   _____

35. dislike; not care for   _____

Exercise E: Writing

Some people say that elephants never forget anything. How is *your* memory? On your own paper, write a short paragraph about a memorable experience that you have had. As you *reminisce*, use THREE Words in your paragraph.

"Gosh, did I pack my toothbrush?   Oh, now where did I put my trunk?"

Quick LIST

abode N.	**belittle** V.	**fugitive** N.	**melancholy** ADJ.	**relish** N., V.
agitate V.	**clamor** N., V.	**linger** V.	**perceive** V.	**reminisce** V.
ample ADJ.	**compassion** N.	**listless** ADJ.	**perish** V.	**timidity** N.

Exercise F: Fill-in

Write the Word that best completes each sentence. Use each word only once.

36. Most people would show _____ for a frightened, lost child by trying to help.

37. My mom and her sisters often _____ about having grown up on a farm.

38. When strangers walk past my house, they _____ my dog, and he runs around barking wildly.

39. The _____ from the house next door suggests that our neighbors are having a party.

40. If a boy is seven, you would _____ him by calling him a baby.

41. Sounds and smells are invisible, but you can _____ them with your ears and nose.

42. To be sure that we would have _____ firewood, we chopped logs for two days.

43. The police are searching for a _____ who is hiding in the swamp.

44. Sally wasn't sad or sick, but she felt too _____ to do anything except sit on the couch and read.

45. It is perfectly normal to feel a bit _____ if your best friend moves away.

46. The last of the blue whales may _____ if people don't help to save these great mammals.

47. I have such a great time with my cousin that I _____ every moment we can be together.

48. When Mel first moved to New York City, his _____ was a small apartment on a busy street.

49. Sometimes, after dinner is over, we _____ at the table and tell stories about what we've done that day.

50. My brother's _____ is obvious from the way he hides behind me whenever someone comes to visit.

Question:
What's another name for a wren house?

Answer:
A bird abode

Question:
What's another name for an egg?

Answer:
A baby bird abode

Word Fun 1!

Word Fun answers start on page 150.

Matching

Match each phrase on the left to the phrase on the right that means the same, or nearly the same, thing.

Question:
Why is tennis such a clamorous game?

____ 1. jolly folly   A. sadness on the streetcar

____ 2. hoard boards   B. survive the sightseeing

____ 3. abhor a chore   C. deeply dislike a duty

____ 4. adorn the horn   D. a risk with a racket

____ 5. endure the tour   E. a big, big, barricade

____ 6. an immense fence   F. beautify the bugle

____ 7. commend a friend   G. worry the worms

____ 8. intimidate the bait   H. fun foolishness

____ 9. a menace at tennis   I. pile up planks

____ 10. melancholy on the trolley   J. praise a pal

Answer:
Because one player or another is always raising a racket!

Boxing

Fill in each set of blanks with a word you know that matches the clue. The boxed letters will spell out the answer to the question on the right.

Question: What do you increase by learning about words and how to use them?

1. one who must do laborious drudgery without pay . . . .

2. to cry in a way that demonstrates acute melancholy . . . . . .

3. to make a jubilant clamor . . . .

4. one who shows timidity and insufficient valor . . . .

5. one who menaces and intimidates others . . . .

6. a shoulder movement that implies a listless attitude . . . .

7. a word that etiquette requires with even a trivial request . . .

8. an immense and ample abode . . . .

9. a luscious course that people relish at meal's end . . . .

10. what one might comprehend if one ponders the clues . . . . .

Puzzling

Identify the **Word** from Unit 1 that fits the clue in each box. (The word's first letter is shown in the answer blank.) In the example, the last three letters change *suddenly*, so the **Word** is . . .

SUDDEN *Ex.* abrupt _____

THHANGERE
4. e _____
   or
   p _____

 **ER**
1. c _____

NOT ENOUG
5. i _____

KEEP MIND
2. p _____

not important
6. t _____

3. i _____

REEEEALLY BIG
7. i _____

Another way to raise a racket

Rhyming

This poem is pretty bad. It'd be better if it rhymed. Substitute a **Word** from Unit 1 for each underlined word. The word you use should make the line rhyme with the one above it.

When I attempt to play the flute,
My need for earplugs is <u>intense</u>.
1. _____

Just listen to me! Every toot'll
Clearly prove my effort's <u>hopeless</u>!
2. _____

Lesson 6 _____

ancestry *AN•ses•tree* NOUN

all of a person's ancestors; one's past family
[I am of Russian *ancestry*.]

balk *BAWK* VERB

1. to stop and stubbornly refuse to move
or act [When horses *balk,* it can be hard to
get them going.]

2. to hesitate due to reluctance [If you dislike
a plan, you may *balk* at going along with it.]

cordial *KOR•jul* ADJECTIVE

warm and friendly [When our guests arrive,
greet them in a *cordial* manner.]

cycle *SY•kul*

NOUN a series of events that occur regularly in
a definite order [The washer goes through
a *cycle* that includes rinsing the clothes.]

VERB to pass through or move in a cycle
[The days *cycle* on—morning, afternoon,
night—and soon a year has passed.]

daze *DAZE*

NOUN a confused, blurry state of
mind [When I first woke up after my operation,
I was in a *daze*.]

VERB to confuse, shock, or stun [Banging
your head can *daze* you, but so can receiving
truly amazing news.]

dilute *dih•LOOT* VERB

to thin down or weaken by mixing with water or
another liquid [Melting ice will *dilute* a drink.]

harass *HAIR•us* or *huh•RAS* VERB

to disturb, worry, or trouble, especially
by continued attacks or through constant
annoyance [Some bill collectors *harass* people
who owe money by calling them late at night.]

inconceivable *in•kun•SEEV•uh•bul*

ADJECTIVE that cannot be thought of, imagined,
or believed [Why anyone would commit such
a terrible crime was *inconceivable* to me.]

mediocre *mee•dee•OH•kur* ADJECTIVE

neither good nor bad; ordinary
[It was a *mediocre* lunch; I
ate it, but I didn't enjoy it.]

opinionated *oh•PIN•yun•ay•tud* ADJECTIVE

stubbornly sticking to one's opinions;
unreasonably sure that one's own opinions
are correct [She is too *opinionated* to listen
to any advice from me.]

sanctuary *SANK•choo•air•ee* NOUN

1. a place where one can find safety or shelter;
also, the safety found there [People from the
country that was being bombed looked for
sanctuary in a neighboring nation.]

2. a place where birds and animals are
protected from hunters [We visited the bird
sanctuary near Riverside Park.]

3. the part of a church or temple used for
worship [There will be a wedding today in
the *sanctuary*.]

shimmer *SHIM•ur* VERB

to shine in an unsteady manner; to gleam
faintly [Have you ever seen a fish jump out of a
lake and *shimmer* in the sunlight?]

studious *STOO•dee•us* ADJECTIVE

devoted to and fond of study; devoted to
gaining knowledge [Her *studious* habits make
her an excellent pupil.]

substantial *sub•STAN•shul* ADJECTIVE

1. strong and solid [Stand on something
substantial that will support your weight.]

2. more than average; large [We won't go
hungry; we have a *substantial* amount of food.]

3. real or actual [Is that just a suspicion, or do
you have *substantial* information?]

wary *WAIR•ee* ADJECTIVE

very careful to avoid danger;
cautious [All children should
be taught to be *wary* of strangers.]

Exercise A: Questions

Write the Word that best answers the question.

1. What does a satin dress or a string of pearls do when light hits it?

   _____

2. What word describes many people who get good grades in school?

   _____

3. What would you call something if you simply couldn't imagine it?

   _____

4. What do cats, people, mice, and foxes look for when they are being chased?

   _____

5. What could you do to thick pancake batter so you could pour it more easily?

   _____

6. What does a traffic light do as it goes from green to yellow to red?

   _____

Exercise B: Synonyms

Write the Word that is a synonym for each set of words.

7. glimmer; twinkle _____

8. protection; shelter _____

9. pester; bother _____

10. outgoing; pleasant _____

11. alert; watchful _____

12. average; fair; so-so _____

13. unbelievable; impossible _____

Exercise C: Antonyms

Write the Word that is an antonym for each set of words.

14. fabulous; wonderful; great _____

15. rude; cold; mean _____

16. descendants; offspring _____

17. reckless; daring; confident _____

18. proceed; continue; go _____

19. rickety; wobbly; weak _____

20. cooperative; flexible _____

21. reasonable; understandable _____

When anything repeats a cycle, it recycles. You've seen the symbol that encourages people to recycle paper, glass, metal, and other materials. It's a circle of arrows.

This symbol represents the cycle that these materials pass through. First, we take a natural resource, such as trees, to make a product, such as paper. Second, we use the product.

Third, we send it back to a factory to be made into another product. Then the cycle starts over again.

Sometimes, the arrows are said to represent the slogan, "Reduce, Reuse, Recycle." This a short way of reminding people to use less stuff, find ways to use it again, and then recycle it.

Exercise D: Other Forms of Words

Use what you know about the Words to choose
the correct answers.

_____ 22. When you speak **cordially** to someone, you usually
     A. frown.   B. stammer.   C. smile.

_____ 23. An animal that is known for being **balky** is
     A. a whale.   B. a mule.   C. an owl.

_____ 24. You would react to something **warily** if it made you feel
     A. nervous.   B. eager.   C. confident.

_____ 25. One person who seems to enjoy engaging in **harassment** is
     A. a bully.   B. a joker.   C. an athlete.

_____ 26. Which of the following are **cyclic**?
     A. accidents   B. the seasons   C. grandparents

_____ 27. In answer to a question, a **dazed** person is most likely to say,
     A. "Huh?"   B. "I'll consider it."   C. "None of
                                               your business."

_____ 28. The Pilgrims' **ancestral** home was
     A. in America.   B. in England.   C. on the ship,
                                               the *Mayflower*.

Exercise E: What Is It?

Write the Word that each clue describes.

29. This is what you do to a can of frozen juice by adding water
or to a cup of coffee by adding cream.

                    _____

30. This is a condition in which someone who is awake doesn't really
know what's happening.

                    _____

31. This describes a brick building or a safe bridge, but it can also
describe a feast or a fact.

                    _____

32. This describes people who are so sure that their views are
right that it's very hard to change their minds.

                    _____

33. This is what little children often do when they're told to do
something they don't want to do.

                    _____

34. This describes those who pay attention in class, do their
homework, and think that education is important.

                    _____

35. This is your parents, grandparents, great-grandparents, and
so on, but it's not your brother or sister.

                    _____

CYCLE JOKES

Some jokes are funny because
they use cycles. Here is one
example—an old joke that
you probably know. Which
part is a cycle, and what
breaks the cycle?

Knock-knock.
Who's there?
Banana.
Knock-knock.
Who's there?
Banana.
Knock-knock.
Who's there?
Banana.
Knock-knock.
Who's there?
Orange.
Orange who?
Orange you glad I
didn't say "banana"?

Exercise F: Fill-in

Write the Word that best completes each sentence. Use each word only once.

36. My puppy's_____ is mixed; her mother is a spaniel, and her father is a beagle.

37. The criminals fled from the police, seeking _____ wherever they could find it.

38. If you have a _____ debt, it will probably take you a long time to repay it.

39. The life _____ of a frog includes three stages—egg, tadpole, and adult.

40. Some boys in our neighborhood _____ my brother whenever he leaves the house, so he doesn't like to go out anymore.

41. My parents aren't satisfied if I get a _____ report card; they want to see A's and B's.

42. Both of my dogs _____ when we get near the vet's office, and I have to drag them.

43. It's hard to convince _____ people that their ideas and attitudes are not the only reasonable ideas and attitudes.

44. Seeing her home go up in flames seemed to _____ the woman, and she watched with no expression on her face.

45. Cats are usually _____ of new surroundings, and it takes a while for them to feel safe.

46. Zoey has been so _____ lately that we've seen her only at school and in the library.

47. When you make mud pies, you must _____ the mud if it's too thick; if it's too thin, you must add more dirt to it.

48. We sat out in the dark and watched moonlight _____ on the surface of the lake.

49. Since the team hadn't lost a game in three years, it was _____ that they would suddenly lose to the last-place team.

50. My friends like visiting my house because my parents are always so _____.

JOKES TO RECYCLE

When you tell a joke, and your friend tells it to someone, and that person tells it again, your joke is being re-cycled. Start a cycle with one of these.

What do you call an ordinary frog?
A mediocre croaker

What do you call a nervous, yellow songbird?
A wary canary

What do you call a fainter gleam?
A dimmer shimmer

Quick LIST

ancestry N.	**cycle** N., V.	**harass** V.	**opinionated** ADJ.	**studious** ADJ.
balk V.	**daze** N., V.	**inconceivable** ADJ.	**sanctuary** N.	**substantial** ADJ.
cordial ADJ.	**dilute** V.	**mediocre** ADJ.	**shimmer** V.	**wary** ADJ.

Lesson 7

appropriate *uh•PRO•pree•ut* ADJECTIVE
suitable, proper [A bathing suit is *appropriate* clothing for the beach but not for school.]

contradict *kon•truh•DIKT* VERB
1. to say that a statement is not true or to say that the opposite is true [When Jane said I started the fight, I had to *contradict* her.]
2. to go against or disagree with [Measurements *contradict* your claim that you are taller.]

fraud *FRAWD* NOUN
1. cheating; dishonest dealing; a trick that is meant to deceive [When my "gold" ring turned green, I knew I was a victim of *fraud*.]
2. a person who is not what he or she pretends to be, or something that is not what it seems to be [That man isn't a real doctor; he's a *fraud*.]

heritage *HAIR•uh•tij* NOUN
something that is passed on from one's ancestors or handed down from the past, either property (money or goods) or something that is not property, such as a way of life or a set of skills [Freedom is part of the *heritage* of all Americans.]

Places such as Mount Rushmore are part of our national heritage.

hostile *HOS•tul* ADJECTIVE
1. referring to an enemy [*Hostile* soldiers captured the fort.]
2. unfriendly; showing hate or dislike [The bully gave him a *hostile* look.]

intelligible *in•TEL•uh•juh•bul* ADJECTIVE
understandable; clear [When you give directions, make sure they are *intelligible*.]

intervene *in•tur•VEEN* VERB
1. to happen or come between [Two weeks will *intervene* between matches.]
2. to come in or between in order to change, stop, or settle [I won't *intervene* in the quarrel.]

invalid *IN•vuh•lid*
NOUN   a sick, weak person who cannot get around, especially one who has been in poor health for a long time [Grandpa has been an *invalid* since he broke his hip.]
ADJECTIVE   not well; weak and sick [They have an *invalid* child at home.]

jostle *JOS•ul* VERB
to push aside or crowd against [Trying to get into the stadium, the eager fans began to *jostle* one another.]

majestic *muh•JES•tik* ADJECTIVE
dignified; noble; grand [The wealthy family lived in a *majestic* home in the country.]

obliging *uh•BLY•jing* ADJECTIVE
ready to do favors; helpful; friendly [Our *obliging* neighbors helped when Mom was sick.]

parch *PARCH* VERB
to make or become hot and dry or thirsty [This sunny, dry weather will *parch* the crops.]

potential *puh•TEN•shul*
ADJECTIVE   possible but not yet actual; capable of becoming real [Let's think of all the *potential* problems involved in moving.]
NOUN   skill or power that may be developed [She has the *potential* to become a champion.]

scurry *SKUR•ee* VERB
to run quickly; to hurry [I'll *scurry* down to the store and be right back.]

shiftless *SHIFT•lus* ADJECTIVE
lazy; careless; good-for-nothing [The *shiftless* man wouldn't even look for a job.]

Exercise A: Synonyms

Write the **Word** that is a synonym for each set of words.

1. deny; oppose _____

2. to interfere; to butt in _____

3. reasonable; right; fitting _____

4. considerate; kind _____

5. to rush; to scamper _____

6. to scorch; to wither _____

7. a phony; a fake; a rip off _____

8. clear; understandable _____

9. to shove; to elbow _____

10. roots; background; culture _____

Exercise B: Antonyms

Write the **Word** that is an antonym for each set of words.

11. common; shabby; humble _____

12. moisten; dampen _____

13. stroll; wander _____

14. hardworking; energetic _____

15. peaceful; friendly; helpful _____

16. uncaring; thoughtless _____

17. healthy; strong; well _____

18. agree; support _____

Exercise C: Completion

Choose the correct answer to complete each sentence.

_____ 19. The people most responsible for your **heritage** are your
   A. family.
   B. friends.
   C. teachers.

_____ 20. If there's a fight and you **intervene**, you
   A. shout.
   B. butt in.
   C. walk away.

_____ 21. You would expect an **invalid** to spend a great deal of time
   A. resting.
   B. working.
   C. studying.

_____ 22. You are most likely to be **jostled** while playing
   A. football.
   B. the piano.
   C. a card game.

_____ 23. People might think you are **shiftless** if you
   A. cheat.
   B. show off.
   C. sleep all day.

_____ 24. One animal that almost always looks **majestic** is a
   A. fox.
   B. lion.
   C. rabbit.

THE LIBERTY BELL is a copy—but not a fraud. The original bell broke soon after arriving from England, where it had been made. In 1753, Philadelphians made a duplicate bell. *That* bell cracked eighty years later. Now the bell is rung only on very special occasions.

Exercise D: *If . . .*

Write the Word that best completes each sentence.

25. If someone avoids any kind of work, doesn't help to get things
    done, and takes advantage of other people, that person is . . . .   _____

26. If a child is smart and hard-working and talented, even if he or
    she hasn't accomplished much yet, that child has a lot of . . . .   _____

27. If a redwood tree rises up to a towering height and is so impressive
    that it takes your breath away, it could be described as being . . . . .   _____

28. If a carpenter working on a roof fell off and broke both of her
    legs, she would probably spend several months as an . . . .   _____

29. If two neighbors dislike each other, pick fights, argue, and try
    to make each other's lives miserable, their relationship is . . . .   _____

Exercise E: *Other Forms of Words*

Use what you know about the Words to choose the correct answers.

____ 30. Which two things are **contradictory**?
      A. hunger and thirst   B. life and death   C. sadness and misery

____ 31. Someone who usually behaves **appropriately** has
      A. a temper.   B. courage.   C. good manners.

____ 32. Which of these things is always **fraudulent**?
      A. a contract   B. a report card   C. a forgery

____ 33. The **intelligibility** of what you say will be increased if you
      A. memorize it.   B. speak slowly.   C. mumble.

____ 34. Which sound is an expression of **hostility**?
      A. groaning   B. snarling   C. giggling

____ 35. When a situation is **potentially** dangerous, the danger is
      A. possible.   B. minor.   C. over.

Exercise F: *Writing*

What part of America's national **heritage** is very special to
you? Is it a right or freedom that you enjoy? Is it a famous
landmark, such as Yellowstone Park or Liberty Island? Is it
a person, such as Harriet Tubman or George Washington?

On your own paper, describe that person, place, or
thing and why it's so special to you. Use at least TWO
Words in your answer.

THE STATUE OF LIBERTY, like the Liberty
Bell, started out in Europe. It was paid for by
French citizens and built in Paris. The
Frenchman who designed it also chose the
appropriate spot for it in New York Bay. The
statue was dedicated in 1886 following
eleven years of construction.

Exercise G: Fill-in
Write the Word that best completes each sentence. Use each word only once.

36. I saw a mouse _____ between some boxes when I turned on the light.

37. Important parts of my people's _____ are dancing, music, and storytelling.

38. Exactly 364 days _____ between one birthday and the next; when there's a leap year, it's 365 days.

39. The road sign warned us of _____ danger from falling rocks.

40. I'm afraid I must _____ you and say that two plus two is *not* five.

41. In nature, nothing is as _____ as the sight of towering, snow-capped mountain peaks.

42. She is so _____ that I don't think she has ever said no when asked to help someone.

43. Yelling and whistling are _____ while watching a game but not while watching a movie.

44. A long hike on a hot day can _____ your throat, so take water with you.

45. My _____ aunt is determined to get well enough to take care of herself.

46. My _____ brother spent the summer doing nothing while everyone else had jobs.

47. I didn't mean to _____ the girl ahead of me in line, but someone bumped me from behind.

48. We discovered that the treasure map was a _____ when all we dug up was a rusty can.

49. Those two _____ nations have been at war with each other for many years.

50. The doctor's explanation was so _____ that I knew exactly what was wrong.

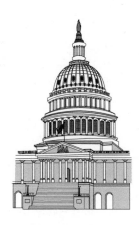

THE U. S. CAPITOL was not even finished when, during the War of 1812, hostile British troops set fire to it. During reconstruction after the war, a dome was added. Then that one was replaced by the present majestic dome in the 1860s when the building was enlarged.

Lesson 8

biodegradable *by•oh•dih•GRAY•duh•bul*
ADJECTIVE   readily broken down or rotted, especially by the action of bacteria   [Paper is *biodegradable*, but most plastic is not.]

clarity *KLAIR•uh•tee*   NOUN
1. clearness in quality or appearance   [The *clarity* of glass is improved when it is cleaned.]
2. clearness in expression or understanding [The rule was stated with *clarity*.]

confine *kun•FINE*   VERB
1. to keep or hold within limits; to restrict [*Confine* your purchases to things on the list.]
2. to keep physically restricted; to shut up [We built a fence to *confine* our dog to the yard.]

ecstasy *EK•stuh•see*   NOUN
very great happiness   [Winning the contest filled me with *ecstasy*.]

exhale *EX•hale*   VERB
1. to breathe out   [When you *exhale* on a cold day, you can see your breath.]
2. to give off, as air, smoke, gas, etc. [Boiling pots of water *exhale* steam.]

grave *GRAVE*   ADJECTIVE
1. important; worthy of being deeply considered   [The city council dealt with many *grave* issues, such as the need for stop lights.]
2. dangerous; threatening   [His illness is *grave*, and I'm very worried.]
3. serious; thoughtful   [The judge spoke to the jury in a *grave* tone.]

A cemetery worker who never smiles is a grave digger.

inflammation *in•fluh•MAY•shun*   NOUN
a hot, red, sore swelling of part of the body [He was troubled by *inflammation* in his knees.]

lurk *LURK*   VERB
to stay hidden, usually ready to attack or spring out suddenly   [At night, many children imagine that monsters *lurk* in their bedroom closet.]

monotonous *muh•NOT•uh•nus*   ADJECTIVE
having little or no change; boring because of sameness   [After a few days, summer vacation became *monotonous*.]

primitive *PRIM•uh•tuv*   ADJECTIVE
1. of or belonging to earliest times   [We are studying *primitive* humans and how they lived.]
2. very simple; like that of earliest times [Clinics in poor nations may be able to provide only *primitive* treatment.]

reel *REEL*   VERB
1. to walk or move unsteadily; to stagger or sway, as from dizziness   [Twirling around can make you *reel*.]
2. to spin around and around; to whirl [When you are dizzy, the room seems to *reel*.]

remnant *REM•nunt*   NOUN
that which remains or is left over   [Mom made pot holders from a *remnant* of cloth.]

surpass *sur•PAS*   VERB
to do better; be greater than; or go beyond [This season's crop of apples should easily *surpass* last year's.]

trial *TRY•ul*
NOUN   1. the act of trying or testing   [Despite a few problems, the new plane did extremely well in its first *trial*.]
NOUN   2. something that causes hardship or suffering   [The illness was a great *trial*.]
ADJECTIVE   of or for a trial or test   [I received a *trial* sample.]

unruly *un•ROO•lee*   ADJECTIVE
hard to control; disobedient   [I dislike babysitting for *unruly* children.]

Exercise A: Questions

Write the **Word** that best answers the question.

1. What describes the people who first invented the wheel and learned to use fire? _____

2. What does rain do to kids on stormy days and illness do to them even on sunny days? _____

3. What do boxers often do as they are about to fall to the mat after being punched? _____

4. What kind of horses buck off their riders and refuse to go into their stalls? _____

5. What does the winner of a race do to the other runners? _____

6. What do you have to do after holding your breath for a while? _____

7. What describes carrots and fish but not rocks or cans? _____

8. What is a characteristic of diamonds but not of gold? _____

My dog Turk likes to lurk in the dark and then bark!

Exercise B: True or False

Circle TRUE or FALSE for each statement.

9. **Unruly** hair is easy to comb, brush, and style. . . . .   TRUE   FALSE

10. An experiment is a kind of **trial**. . . . .   TRUE   FALSE

11. People **exhale** when they blow out candles. . . . .   TRUE   FALSE

12. **Biodegradable** garbage is bad for the environment. . . . .   TRUE   FALSE

13. One sign of good health is **inflammation**. . . . .   TRUE   FALSE

14. Getting hit on the head might make you **reel**. . . . .   TRUE   FALSE

ANN:
My report on biodegradable materials got an A. What about yours?

DAN:
Mine was D-gradable.

Exercise C: Synonyms

Write the **Word** that could be use in place of each underlined word or phrase. This exercise continues on the next page.

15. Many zoos <u>cage</u> animals in small spaces; others give them more room. _____

16. Because the work was <u>always the same</u>, I couldn't make myself keep doing it. _____

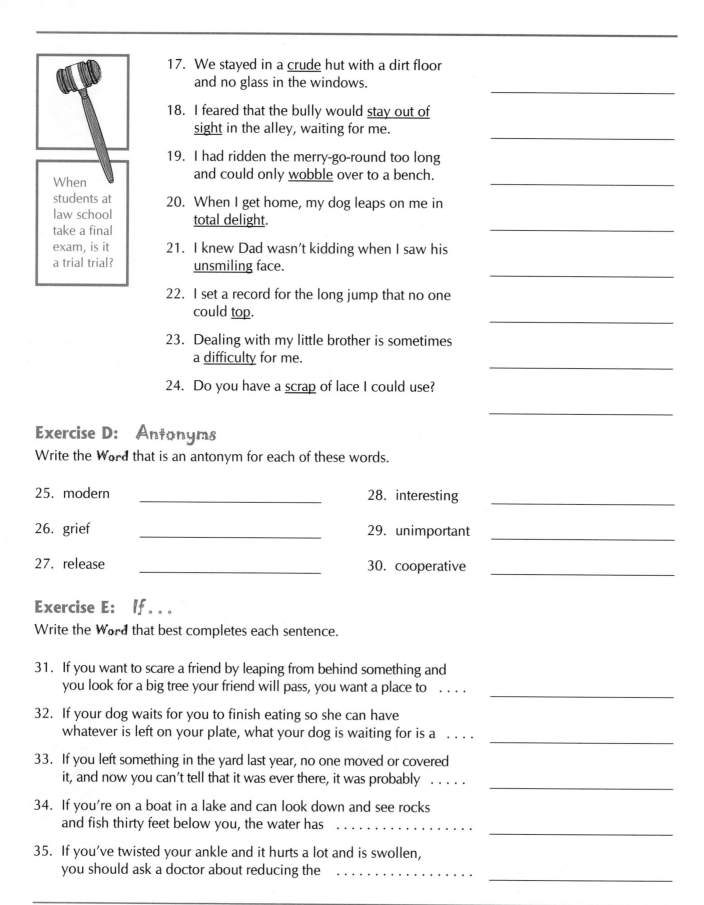

When students at law school take a final exam, is it a trial trial?

17. We stayed in a crude hut with a dirt floor and no glass in the windows.

_____

18. I feared that the bully would stay out of sight in the alley, waiting for me.

_____

19. I had ridden the merry-go-round too long and could only wobble over to a bench.

_____

20. When I get home, my dog leaps on me in total delight.

_____

21. I knew Dad wasn't kidding when I saw his unsmiling face.

_____

22. I set a record for the long jump that no one could top.

_____

23. Dealing with my little brother is sometimes a difficulty for me.

_____

24. Do you have a scrap of lace I could use?

_____

Exercise D: Antonyms

Write the Word that is an antonym for each of these words.

25. modern   _____

26. grief   _____

27. release   _____

28. interesting   _____

29. unimportant _____

30. cooperative _____

Exercise E: If . . .

Write the Word that best completes each sentence.

31. If you want to scare a friend by leaping from behind something and you look for a big tree your friend will pass, you want a place to . . . .

_____

32. If your dog waits for you to finish eating so she can have whatever is left on your plate, what your dog is waiting for is a . . . .

_____

33. If you left something in the yard last year, no one moved or covered it, and now you can't tell that it was ever there, it was probably . . . . .

_____

34. If you're on a boat in a lake and can look down and see rocks and fish thirty feet below you, the water has . . . .

_____

35. If you've twisted your ankle and it hurts a lot and is swollen, you should ask a doctor about reducing the . . . .

_____

Quick LIST

biodegradable ADJ.
clarity N.
confine V.

ecstasy N.
exhale V.
grave ADJ.
inflammation N.

lurk V.
monotonous ADJ.
primitive ADJ.
reel V.

remnant N.
surpass V.
trial N., ADJ.
unruly ADJ.

Exercise F: Fill-in

Write the Word that best completes each sentence. Use each word only once.

36. A panther may _____ in the jungle, waiting for prey.

37. I enjoy learning about dinosaurs and other _____ forms of life.

38. The candidates were asked to _____ their speeches to ten minutes apiece.

39. I reacted with _____ to my parents' plan to spend the day at an amusement park.

40. A beautiful, old town hall is the only _____ of the town's former glory.

41. The factory smokestacks _____ so much smoke that the entire sky is blackened.

42. Telephones today allow one to hear with perfect _____ what someone a thousand miles away is saying.

43. Delivering newspapers can be a _____ job because you go to the same places every day.

44. The world seemed to _____ when I got to my feet after rolling down the hill.

45. A flock of frightened sheep can be quite _____, and a trained sheep dog is a big help in controlling them.

46. The problem is _____; no one knows if it can be solved, and everyone fears the worst.

47. The carnival was so successful that the profit will _____ last year's by several thousand dollars.

48. My parents buy _____ detergent because, unlike ordinary soap, it breaks down and doesn't harm the environment.

49. Losing their home in a tornado was a _____ for my aunt and uncle, but their lives are back to normal now.

50. The _____ in my grandfather's hands has become so bad that he has had to give up playing golf and baking bread.

Mrs. *Beal* slipped on a *peel* and began to *reel*. How does she *feel*? She hurt her *heel*. "It's no big *deal*," said Mrs. *Beal*.

DAD: Turn down the sound! It's making my head spin! What is that stuff anyway?

DAUGHTER: Rock-and-reel.

Lesson 9 _____

bilingual *by•LING•gwul* ADJECTIVE
having or using two languages [Luca,
who spends every summer in Italy with his
grandparents, has grown up *bilingual*.]

dreary *DREER•ee* ADJECTIVE
gloomy, sad, or dull [My aunt's stories
about her difficult childhood are always long
and *dreary*.]

glint *GLINT*
NOUN a beam, glow, or flash [I saw a *glint* of
light in the distance.]
VERB to beam, glow, or flash [Look at the
sunlight *glint* through the trees.]

glutton *GLUT•un* NOUN
a person who overeats; a greedy eater
[Don't be such a *glutton;* leave some for us!]

incomprehensible *in•kom•prih•HEN•suh•bul*
ADJECTIVE not understandable [How anyone
can be cruel to a child is *incomprehensible*.]

infancy *IN•fun•see* NOUN
1. babyhood [*Infancy* is a time of great growth.]
2. early period of existence or development
[In the 1780s, America was in its *infancy*.]

instinct *IN•stingkt* NOUN
1. a natural knowledge, feeling, or way of
acting that is not learned but, instead, is present
from birth; a natural, inner force [Most dogs
have an *instinct* to defend their homes.]
2. a natural ability, talent, or tendency
[Mara has an *instinct* for knowing what colors
will look good together.]

knowledgeable *NOL•ij•uh•bul* ADJECTIVE
having knowledge; intelligent [My dad has
traveled a great deal and is *knowledgeable* about
other countries.]

manipulate *muh•NIP•yoo•late* VERB
1. to work with the hands or with a machine,
especially with skill [Potters *manipulate* clay.]
2. to manage or control cleverly, often by
cheating or being tricky [He used lies to
manipulate us into doing what he wanted.]

mimic *MIM•uk*
VERB 1. to copy or imitate very closely
[The dancers *mimic* the instructor's steps.]
VERB 2. to make fun of by imitating
[It always upset me when other children would
mimic the odd way I walked.]
NOUN one who mimics [A monkey is a good
mimic, which is why people say, "Monkey see,
monkey do."]

mystify *MIS•tuh•fy* VERB
to bewilder or puzzle [This story will *mystify*
you until the end.]

quake *KWAKE*
VERB to shake or tremble [The odd noises in
the dark house made me *quake*.]
NOUN a short form of *earthquake* [The *quake*
damaged many buildings.]

shun *SHUN* VERB
to avoid completely; to keep away from
[I would advise you to *shun* anyone who behaves
like a bully.]

summon *SUM•un* VERB
1. to call or send for; to call together
[*Summon* everyone for a meeting.]
2. to gather; to stir to activity [You need to
summon your courage.]

zeal *ZEEL* NOUN
a strong, eager desire or effort; great
enthusiasm [My partner and I began our
project with *zeal*.]

_____

3 Smelly Questions

1. How are a skunk and
a bad mimic alike?

2. What is a skunk when
it's in its infancy?

3. How does a lost skunk
find its way home?

Exercise A: Questions

Write the **Word** that best answers the question.

1. What do you see when sunlight reflects off of a piece of metal? _____

2. What word describes a rainy afternoon when there's nothing interesting to do? _____

3. What stage of life are people in when they use a playpen and a high chair? _____

4. What is a treehouse likely to do during a really violent thunderstorm? _____

5. What word describes a class in which instructions are given in both Spanish and English? _____

6. What do people tend to do to those of whom they strongly disapprove? _____

7. What quality is found in those who truly love what they are doing? _____

8. What does a spoiled child try to do to his parents to get his or her own way? _____

9. What do teachers, tutors, and instructors hope their students can become? _____

10. What does the children's game "Follow the Leader" require players to do? _____

11. What makes a bird build a nest or a cat chase mice? _____

Exercise B: Synonyms

Write the **Word** that is a synonym for each set of words.

12. shiver; wobble _____

13. baffle; confuse _____

14. ignore; reject _____

15. big eater; hog _____

16. sparkle; twinkle _____

17. depressing; unhappy _____

18. copycat; echo; parrot _____

3 Stinky Answers
1. They both stink. 2. A little stinker
3. By instinkt.

Exercise C: Yes or No

Circle YES or NO for each question.

19. Are you likely to enjoy reading a book that is ***incomprehensible*** to you? . . . .   YES   NO

20. Does a child who is playing house ***mimic*** the behavior of grown-ups? . . . .   YES   NO

21. If someone has an ***instinct*** for drawing, is the person good at it? . . . .   YES   NO

22. Is a ***bilingual*** person someone who can both read and write? . . . .   YES   NO

23. Would you do well in school subjects that ***mystify*** you? . . . .   YES   NO

24. Would you ***manipulate*** clay to make a figure from it? . . . . .   YES   NO

25. Do you ***summon*** someone you want to avoid? . . . .   YES   NO

26. Do you ***quake*** when you feel confident? . . . .   YES   NO

27. Can a ***glint*** cut you? . . . .   YES   NO

Exercise D: Antonyms

Write the Word that is an antonym for each set of words.

28. adulthood; maturity

29. clear; obvious; reasonable

30. dismiss; send away

31. ignorant; inexperienced

32. reluctance; boredom; unconcern

33. explain; make clear

34. bright; cheerful; exciting

35. picky eater; dieter

Exercise E: Writing

Most of us know a lot about *something*. What are you ***knowledgeable*** about? Computers? State capitals? Skunks? Making pickles? How did you learn what you know? What do you do, or plan to do, with your knowledge? On your own paper, use THREE or more Words to describe something that you are knowledgeable about.

Question:
Why did the math textbook feel so dreary?

DIVIDE
16 + 13   27 + 2   ADD
144 − 26   15
SUBTRACT   × 4
18 ÷ 2

Answer: Because it had so many problems.

Quick LIST

bilingual ADJ.
dreary ADJ.
glint N., V.
glutton N.
incomprehensible ADJ.
infancy N.
instinct N.
knowledgeable ADJ.
manipulate V.
mimic V., N.
mystify V.
quake V., N.
shun V.
summon V.
zeal N.

Exercise F: Fill-in

Write the **Word** that best completes each sentence.
Use each word only once.

Question:

What lies at the bottom of the ocean and quakes?

36. She spoke so fast that what she said was _____ to me.

37. We formed our club two months ago, so it's still in its _____.

38. I'm _____ because my family speaks German at home, but I speak English in school.

39. When my parents _____ me, I know I'd better go see what they want.

40. It would surely _____ you to find a pony in your bedroom, wouldn't it?

41. All I could do was stand there and _____ with fear when I saw a rattlesnake on a nearby rock.

42. She was in such a _____ mood that even a visit from her best friend didn't cheer her up.

43. Patrick Henry showed his _____ for American independence when he said, "Give me liberty, or give me death!"

44. My brother is such a _____ that we never have to worry about what to do with leftovers.

45. Our neighbor is quite _____ about plants and can give advice about any gardening problem.

46. Some dogs have such a strong _____ for herding that they even try to herd groups of playing children.

47. A _____ from something shiny in the grass caught my eye, and that's how I found my lost bracelet.

48. Geri was able to _____ me into going along with her plans even though I hadn't wanted to.

49. Bill squinted his eyes and put his hands on his hips to _____ how Dad looks when he's angry.

50. My friends began to _____ me when they thought I had gotten them in trouble, and I spent a lonely week before they learned the truth.

Answer: A nervous wreck

Lesson 10 _____

anonymous *uh•NON•uh•mus* ADJECTIVE

1. with no name known; unknown [Many of our best-known nursery rhymes are by *anonymous* poets.]

2. given or written by someone whose name is not provided [The message was *anonymous*, and I never found out who sent it.]

anxiety *ang•ZY•uh•tee* NOUN

a feeling of worry; uneasy concern or fear [I had some *anxiety* about going to a new school, but it didn't last long.]

beneficial *ben•uh•FISH•ul* ADJECTIVE

helpful; providing a benefit [Drinking milk is quite *beneficial* for bones.]

bounteous *BOWN•tee•us* ADJECTIVE

1. given freely; generous [Some rich people give *bounteous* help to the poor.]

2. plentiful; more than enough [We prepared *bounteous* food for the picnic.]

dishearten *dis•HAR•tun* VERB

to cause to lose spirit or hope; to discourage [Don't let one failure *dishearten* you.]

enthusiast *en•THOO•zee•ust* NOUN

a person with a strong liking for or interest in something; a devoted supporter [Mariana is an in-line *enthusiast* who skates every single day.]

Joe says *everyone* skates and Mariana ought to show more individuality. Joe himself can't go one single block without falling forty times.

individuality

in•duh•vij•oo•AL•uh•tee NOUN

qualities that make one person or thing different from others [People often use clothing to express their *individuality*.]

leeway *LEE•way* NOUN

1. more money, time, etc., than is known to be needed [The price of admission was five dollars, but I took six to give myself a little *leeway*.]

2. room for freedom of action [I have to dress neatly for school, but I have a lot of *leeway* in choosing exactly what to wear.]

liberate *LIH•bur•ate* VERB

to set free [One of the North's goals in the Civil War was to *liberate* the slaves.]

receptacle *ree•SEP•tuh•kul* NOUN

something that receives and contains something else [Hand me that bucket or some other *receptacle* to hold these peaches.]

relic *REL•ik* NOUN

a thing or part that remains from the past [That beautiful old sword is a *relic* from the Revolutionary War.]

replenish *ree•PLEN•ish* VERB

to fill or supply again [We have to stop to *replenish* our gas supply before we get back on the highway.]

scrawny *SKRAW•nee* ADJECTIVE

unusually thin; bony [When we found the cub, he was *scrawny* from lack of food.]

taunt *TAWNT*

NOUN an insulting remark; a gesture or statement that makes fun of someone or something ["I don't want to hear one single *taunt* directed at the other team," said our coach at the pep rally.]

VERB to make fun of in an insulting way ["But what if they *taunt* us?" Joe asked.]

unattainable *un•uh•TANE•uh•bul* ADJECTIVE

unable to be reached or achieved [With our best player out of the competition, victory seemed *unattainable*.]

Exercise A: Completion
Choose the correct answer to complete each sentence.

____ 1. You might ask someone to **liberate** you if you were
   A. tired.
   B. thirsty.
   C. trapped.

____ 2. A stamp **enthusiast** is most likely to be someone who
   A. designs stamps.
   B. collects stamps.
   C. uses a lot of stamps.

____ 3. If something is **unattainable** for you, you will never
   A. want it.
   B. have it.
   C. forget it.

____ 4. An object that is used as a **receptacle** on a dinner table is a
   A. bowl.
   B. knife.
   C. tablecloth.

____ 5. To **replenish** a supply of cereal, you would
   A. eat it.
   B. buy more.
   C. put it away.

____ 6. One place that usually contains a **relic** is a
   A. bakery.
   B. hospital.
   C. museum.

Joe says Ned is scrawny. Ned says, "Not for long. And, anyway, look who's talking!"

Exercise B: Synonyms
Write the Word that is a synonym for each of these words.

7. originality _____

8. holder _____

9. release _____

10. antique _____

11. unknown _____

12. mock _____

13. skinny _____

14. nervousness _____

Exercise C: Fill-in
Write the correct adjective Word to complete each sentence.

15. The food at a feast is

_____.

16. A stray cat often looks

_____.

17. Exercise and medicine are

_____.

18. A valentine that isn't signed is

_____.

19. The goal of never making mistakes is

_____.

Exercise D: What Is It?

Write the Word that each rhymed clue describes.

20. I watch every basketball game that I can.
    I'm crazy for basketball. I am a fan.

    _____

21. This could be a basket or a barrel or a box,
    And, when a fox is eating, it's the stomach of the fox!

    _____

22. If you allow an hour, though that's more time than you need,
    The extra time will give you this. Some "slack" is good, indeed!

    _____

23. If you don't let the problems that you face do this to you,
    Then you do not give up. You're not a quitter, that is true.

    _____

24. This makes Frank different from Pablo or Mike.
    It is not found when all things are alike.

    _____

25. This could be a fossil or an arrowhead or pot.
    It could be almost anything, but modern it is not.

    _____

"Joe, is
it okay if
I stand up
now? . . . Joe?"

Big brothers can cause big anxiety.

Exercise E: Antonyms

Write the Word that is an antonym for each set of words.

26. harmful; dangerous

    _____

27. capture; trap

    _____

28. to cheer; to inspire

    _____

29. confidence; calmness

    _____

30. plump; chubby

    _____

31. compliment; praise

    _____

32. sameness

    _____

33. to use up; to empty

    _____

34. stingy; miserly

    _____

35. strictness; narrowness

    _____

Quick LIST

anonymous ADJ.	**bounteous** ADJ.	**individuality** N.	**receptacle** N.	**scrawny** ADJ.
anxiety N.	**dishearten** V.	**leeway** N.	**relic** N.	**taunt** N., V.
beneficial ADJ.	**enthusiast** N.	**liberate** V.	**replenish** V.	**unattainable** ADJ.

Exercise F: Fill-in

Write the Word that best completes each sentence. Use each word only once.

36. Chris and Nicky are identical twins, but their _____ is obvious when they talk about their interests, which are quite different.

37. Wearing thick socks is _____ in preventing blisters on runners' feet.

38. Because the gift to the homeless shelter was _____, no one knew whom to thank.

39. My _____ made my heart thump and pound, and I even started to tremble.

40. A badly lopsided score like 102–50 can really _____ the team that's behind.

41. It's time to _____ the supply cabinet because we're out of almost everything.

42. Due to the good weather, the garden produced a _____ crop of tomatoes.

43. We dug up a cannonball, a _____ of the American Revolution, while working in the field.

44. This great big glass jar will make the perfect _____ for my marble collection.

45. "Aw, what a crybaby!" was the _____ I heard from some children on the playground.

46. We will trap and cage the raccoons and then _____ them in the wild, far away.

47. My sister, who is a car _____, can identify the make and model of any car she sees.

48. I expected Lauren to be weak because she's so _____, but she's surprisingly strong.

49. Do we have any _____ in what topic our paper can be on, or does it have to be one of the topics on this list?

50. Joe says my goal of becoming a quarterback is _____ because I can't pass at all.

Joe says that Chris's best sport is soccer and that Nicky is better at basketball.

But Joe admits he can't tell them apart, and it might be the other way around!

So what does Joe know about anything anyway?

Word Fun 2!

Digging

Each sentence suggests a **Word** from Unit 2. The word itself is buried in the sentence. Find the word and underline it. (An example is done for you.) These are the words you need to dig up:

confine   daze   hostile   reel
cordial   dishearten   parch   shun

Ex: Jill's enthusiasm, eagerness, and spirit ama<u>ze all</u> who see her.

1. Billy and I can't stand each other, so when I got to the party and realized he was the host, I left immediately.

2. Wilma absolutely refused to even *look* at that food. She put the dish under her napkin.

3. Although Stan is trying hard to break my record, I always say hello in a warm and friendly way.

4. Robin Hood gasped, "Water, water! I need more than just a sip. Archery can be hot, dry work!"

5. I can't believe how loud the crowd is. Hear ten thousand fans yelling for the other team, and you lose your confidence!

6. Maria feels trapped when she has to stay in her room doing arithmetic on fine days.

7. Miguel was so shocked when he scored a zero that he felt numb and in a fog.

8. Bumping my head made me stagger, wobble, and sway as if my legs were elastic.

Matching

Match the phrases that are . . .

____ 1. to liberate a playmate

____ 2. to jostle the fossil

____ 3. wary of vocabulary

____ 4. to applaud the frauds

____ 5. truly unruly

____ 6. to mean to intervene

____ 7. a mediocre soaker

____ 8. a merry sanctuary

Naming

Match each person's . . .

____ 1. Ann Onnimus

____ 2. Benny Fishul

____ 3. Stu D. Uss

____ 4. Lee Way

____ 5. X. Hale

____ 6. Clara T.

____ 7. Mim Ick

____ 8. Ma Jestic

____ 9. Harry Tage

____ 10. Miss T. Fye

Puzzling

Identify the **Word** from Unit 2 that fits the clue in each box. The word's first letter is shown in the answer blank.

| SAME OLD THING |
| SAME OLD THING |
| SAME OLD THING |
| SAME OLD THING |
| SAME OLD THING |
| SAME OLD THING |
| SAME OLD THING |

1. __m_____

closest in meaning.

A. to intend to interrupt

B. to free a friend

C. a happy hideout

D. to cheer for the cheaters

E. watchful of words

F. a so-so squirt gun

G. definitely disobedient

H. to bump the
   brontosaurus bones

Rhyming

Make each set of lines rhyme (and have a poetic rhythm) by substituting a **Word** from Unit 2 for the underlined words.

1. You will bust every zipper and pop every button
   If you don't stop being the world's biggest
   <u>overeating, greedy pig</u>.

   _____

2. Everything we saw or did, my cousin loved or hated.
   She had strong feelings all the time. That girl's
   <u>narrow-minded and stubborn about her own ideas</u>!

   _____

name to the description it goes best with.

A. He's always saying, "Cut me some slack!"

B. He's always breathing sighs of relief.

C. Her behavior puzzles everyone.

D. Nobody knows who she is.

E. She's definitely a copycat.

F. He's always doing homework.

G. She's a magnificent and dignified lady.

H. She's direct, accurate, and easy to understand.

I. He's always helping people by doing good deeds.

J. He'll draw his family tree for anyone who will look at it.

Seeing the hostile dragon exhale, Sir Pass fears
he may not live up to his name. After all,
his disheartened (and parched) buddies,
Sir Vive and Sir Ender, have already
fled to sanctuary in the castle.

JUST ADD
WATER

2. d _____

Happen over and over and over and over again.

3. c _____

Lesson 11

absolute *AB•suh•loot* ADJECTIVE

complete; entire; total [My parents insist on *absolute* obedience.]

blunder *BLUN•dur*

NOUN a foolish or stupid mistake [I made an embarrassing *blunder*.]

VERB **1.** to make a blunder [I hoped I wouldn't *blunder* during my speech.]

VERB **2.** to move clumsily or carelessly [Make sure not to *blunder* off the path.]

calamity *kuh•LAM•uh•tee* NOUN

a terrible event that causes great harm or destruction [The hurricane was a *calamity*.]

Question:
What happened when the hiker blundered into the path of the porcupine?

Answer: It was an absolute quill-amity!

devour *dih•VOWR* VERB

1. to eat, especially to eat very hungrily [I will *devour* my lunch today.]

2. to destroy by using up [Active children can *devour* every last bit of a parent's energy.]

enchant *en•CHANT* VERB

1. to cast a spell over; to use magic on [In the story, a wizard was able to *enchant* a prince.]

2. to delight greatly; to charm [Sara's sweetness and humor *enchant* all who meet her.]

illiteracy *ih•LIT•ur•uh•see* NOUN

lack of education; especially, not knowing how to read and write [My brother teaches adults who want to overcome *illiteracy*.]

incite *in•SITE* VERB

to urge or stir to action [I hope my speech can *incite* people to work on solving the problem.]

instantaneous *in•stun•TAY•nee•us* ADJECTIVE

done or happening in an instant [The effect was *instantaneous*.]

presumption *prih•ZUMP•shun* NOUN

1. a belief; something that is taken for granted; something one presumes [My *presumption* is that there will be food at the party.]

2. annoying or unpleasant boldness or nerve [Mark had the *presumption* to get right in our car even though he hadn't been offered a ride.]

refuge *REF•yooj* NOUN

1. protection from danger, difficulty, or annoyance [We found *refuge* from the rain.]

2. a place of shelter or safety [Our cat's *refuge* from the visiting dog was a closet shelf.]

segment *SEG•munt* NOUN

one of the parts into which something is divided or can be separated [Could I have a *segment* of that orange?]

strew *STROO* VERB

1. to spread about here and there [The wind will *strew* this litter all over the park.]

2. to cover with something scattered or sprinkled [If you *strew* sawdust on spilled oil, it will soak up the oil.]

supplement *SUP•luh•ment*

NOUN something added to make a thing more complete or better [Our Sunday newspaper has a *supplement* that gives information about local entertainment.]

VERB to add to or complete [You could *supplement* the speech with a video.]

uncanny *un•KAN•ee* ADJECTIVE

so remarkable as to seem unnatural; very strange; mysterious [My dog has an *uncanny* ability to know when I'm sad.]

venture *VEN•chur*

NOUN a risky activity or undertaking [The business *venture* failed.]

VERB **1.** to dare to say or do [I'm not sure, but I'll *venture* a guess.]

VERB **2.** to go in spite of some risk [Let's *venture* up the mountain.]

Exercise A: *If . . .*

Write the **Word** that best completes each sentence.

1. If you dreamed that something odd would happen and then it did, or if you met a new student with the same name and birthday as yours, that event would be . . . . _____

2. If it is so quiet that you can almost hear your heart beat, if no one talks, coughs, or shuffles around, the silence is . . . . _____

3. If a plumber is joining pieces of pipe to make one long pipe, each short piece of pipe is a . . . . _____

4. If the dinner you order at a restaurant doesn't seem big enough, the salad you get to go along with it is a . . . . _____

5. If a city is badly damaged by an earthquake and thousands of people are killed or hurt, the earthquake is a . . . . _____

6. If you often see a woman playing or walking with a particular child, the idea that she is the child's mother is a reasonable . . . . . . _____

7. If a man buys a large piece of land in the hope of making a profit by selling parts of it to different people, his action is a . . . . _____

8. If you saw a friend eat four sandwiches, three apples, and a whole pie, you'd be surprised by what your friend could . . . . _____

Exercise B: Synonyms

Write the **Word** that is closest in meaning to each set of phrases.

9. put your foot in it; make a slip of the tongue; goof up _____

10. gobble up; dig in; shovel up; work your jaws _____

11. take a chance; go out on a limb; run a risk _____

12. egg on; light a fire under; whip into action _____

13. quick as a wink; in no time flat; in a flash _____

Exercise C: Antonyms

Write the **Word** that is an antonym for each set of words and phrases. This exercise continues on the next page.

14. subtract; take away _____

15. annoy; irritate; bore _____

16. gather; collect; pick up _____

Question:
What happened to the cat that devoured a ball of yarn?

Answer: She had mittens.

17. learning; education; knowledge   _____

18. calm down; discourage; soothe   _____

19. shyness; timidity; hesitation   _____

20. slow; gradual; after a while   _____

21. ordinary; normal; natural   _____

22. partial; imperfect; faulty   _____

23. exposure; danger; peril   _____

Exercise D: Completion

Choose the correct answer to complete each sentence.

_____ 24. The most common reaction to a **calamity** is
     A. grief.   B. relief.   C. boredom.

_____ 25. One place that is meant to be a **refuge** is a
     A. dump.   B. fort.   C. store.

_____ 26. If a statement is the **absolute** truth, it is
     A. a lie.   B. the truth.   C. a good guess.

_____ 27. Someone who makes a **blunder** usually feels
     A. afraid.   B. proud.   C. embarrassed.

_____ 28. Something that a person might **strew** in a garden is
     A. seeds.   B. blossoms.   C. a hoe and rake.

_____ 29. A person could help someone suffering from **illiteracy** by being that person's
     A. tutor.   B. nurse.   C. driver.

Question:
What happened to the fellow who was devoured by a cow?

Answer:
He became the man in the moo.

Exercise F: Writing

If you could **enchant** everyone in the whole world to do something, what would it be? On your own paper, explain your answer in a paragraph using THREE **Words**.

Exercise E: Yes or No

Circle YES or NO for each question.

30. Do writers tend to suffer from **illiteracy**? . . . .   YES   NO

31. Is a **segment** pretty much the same thing as a section? . . . . .   YES   NO

32. Would you enjoy watching a movie that **enchants** you? . . . .   YES   NO

33. Is a wildlife **refuge** a place where people go to hunt animals? . . . . . .   YES   NO

34. Is asking people to "please settle down" a good way to **incite** them? . . . . .   YES   NO

35. Does a raging forest fire **devour** trees, bushes, and maybe even animals? . . . . . .   YES   NO

Exercise G: Fill-in

Write the **Word** that best completes each sentence. Use each word only once.

36. Let's not _____ across the ice; it seems too thin to support our weight.

37. Some doctors think it's a good idea to _____ one's diet with vitamin pills.

38. Most sharks _____ live fish, including other sharks, and a shark's most common natural enemy is a larger shark.

39. My worst baking _____ occurred when I forgot to put the sugar in my father's birthday cake.

40. The student did his best to _____ the audience to protest the rising costs of going to college.

41. Fingerprints provided _____ proof that the suspect had been at the scene of the crime.

42. _____ tends to be common in poor countries where there is little money for schools.

43. Her answer to my question was _____; the moment the words left my mouth, she blurted out the answer.

44. War is a _____ that ruins the lives of many people.

45. We plan to _____ rose petals along the aisle that the bride and groom will take to the altar.

46. There is something _____ about my best friend's ability to read my mind.

47. My _____ is that the train will be late today since it has never yet been on time.

48. The soldiers sought _____ from the enemy fire wherever they could: behind trees, in ditches, and behind an old barn.

49. I need to memorize the name and purpose of each _____ of an ant's body for tomorrow's test.

50. If I could wave a wand, say "abracadabra," and _____ my mother, we'd never, ever have canned peas for dinner again.

Quick LIST

absolute ADJ.
blunder N., V.
calamity N.
devour V.
enchant V.
illiteracy N.
incite V.
instantaneous ADJ.
presumption N.
refuge N.
segment N.
strew V.
supplement N., V.
uncanny ADJ.
venture N., V.

Question:
Why did the golfer take a supplementary pair of socks with him?

Answer: In case he got a hole in one

Lesson 12

adequate *AD•ih•kwit* ADJECTIVE

good enough for the situation [I'm not the best pitcher on the team, but I'm *adequate* for today's game.]

agony *AG•uh•nee* NOUN

great pain of body or mind [A broken leg can cause *agony*.]

audible *AW•duh•bul* ADJECTIVE

heard or capable of being heard [The cheeping of the baby birds was barely *audible* from the ground.]

brawny *BRAW•nee* ADJECTIVE

muscular; strong [The *brawny* lumberjack could swing an ax as if it were a candy cane.]

cantankerous *kan•TANG•kur•us* ADJECTIVE

never agreeable; difficult to deal with [The guy at the bookstore is so *cantankerous*, I hate going in there.]

decade *DEK•ade* NOUN

a ten-year period [The sixties was a *decade* of restlessness and change.]

exquisite *EX•kwih•zit* ADJECTIVE

1. extremely lovely; delicately beautiful [Your roses are *exquisite*.]

2. highly admirable; excellent [His manners are *exquisite*.]

ferocious *fuh•ROH•shus* ADJECTIVE

savagely cruel; extremely fierce or violent [A hungry lion is a *ferocious* beast.]

flourish *FLUR•ish*

NOUN a fancy or showy motion; a dramatic, sweeping movement [I set the decorated cake down on the table with a *flourish*.]

VERB to grow and develop well; to be successful [Grandma is a wonderful gardener, and all her plants *flourish*.]

hearsay *HEER•say* NOUN

gossip; something that is not known directly but from being repeated [You shouldn't believe what Jeri tells you about Hank; it's only *hearsay*.]

impartial *im•PAR•shul* ADJECTIVE

fair; not taking one side or the other [Lawyers aren't supposed to be *impartial*, but judges are.]

mar *MAR* VERB

to damage; to keep from being perfect [Be careful not to *mar* the finish of the car by scratching it.]

opaque *oh•PAKE* ADJECTIVE

blocking light; not capable of being seen through [An *opaque* paint will cover those marks completely.]

ransack *RAN•sak* VERB

to search thoroughly through [If you're going to *ransack* that drawer, put everything back!]

texture *TEX•chur* NOUN

the surface qualities of something; the way something feels to the touch [The *texture* of the cloth was rough and a little scratchy.]

A VERY SILLY (AND TOTALLY MADE-UP) STORY ABOUT HEARSAY

In 1883, a kind-hearted rancher named Billie B. Boop accidentally invented a new "language." To keep her sheep from feeling mental agony, Boop told her ranch hands that it was time to "ear-shay the eep-shay." The hands liked this way of talking and called it Earshay.

A decade later, a traveling salesman brought Earshay back east but mistakenly called it Hearsay. Today, that word has a different meaning, and Earshay is called Pig Latin. (Some people want Congress to pass a law to name it Sheep Latin, but that's another story.)

One of Oop-bay's eep-shays

Exercise A: True or False

Circle TRUE or FALSE for each statement.

1. It would be a compliment to describe someone's manners as being **exquisite**. . . .   TRUE   FALSE

2. You can be sure that information you get from **hearsay** is absolutely true. . . . . . .   TRUE   FALSE

3. Umpires and referees are always supposed to be **impartial**. . . . .   TRUE   FALSE

4. A **brawny** person would need help carrying a suitcase. . . . .   TRUE   FALSE

5. The time from 1975 to 1987 was a **decade**. . . . .   TRUE   FALSE

6. Velvet and denim have different **textures**. . . . .   TRUE   FALSE

Exercise B: Antonyms

Write the Word that is an antonym for each set of words.

7. repair; fix; protect   _____

8. crude; plain; ordinary   _____

9. gentle; tame; harmless   _____

10. weaken; fade; collapse   _____

11. scrawny; weak; delicate   _____

12. silent; hushed; noiseless   _____

13. transparent; clear as glass   _____

14. one-sided; unjust; slanted   _____

A MAR(S) STORY

On July 3, 1776, a spaceship landed near Independence Hall in Philadelphia. The pilot introduced himself or herself and apologized for interrupting whatever was going on.

A ferocious frown on his face, Ben Franklin said, "Sir or madam! I don't care if you're from Mars! That apology is not adequate. You have marred our whole ceremony! Now we'll have to do it all over again tomorrow!"

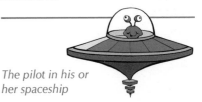

The pilot in his or her spaceship

Exercise C: Analogies

Write the letter of the word pair that completes each analogy.

_____ 15. **mar**: ruin ::
  A. rip : tear
  B. hear : see
  C. grow : shrink
  D. dampen : soak

_____ 16. year : **decade** :
  A. dime : dollar
  B. day : week
  C. ounce : pound
  D. finger : hand

_____ 17. look : **ransack** :
  A. listen : hear
  B. clean : scrub
  C. talk : whisper
  D. ask : answer

_____ 18. **texture** : touch :
  A. giggle : laugh
  B. cloth : fabric
  C. sound : hearing
  D. sheep : wool

_____ 19. **audible** : ears :
  A. visible : eyes
  B. lonely : alone
  C. delicious : food
  D. painful : blisters

_____ 20. **agony** : pain :
  A. itch : lotion
  B. beauty : ugliness
  C. cat : kitten
  D. terror : fear

In 1922, poet H. H. Hoop visited his hometown, Mojo, Maine. There he saw his school sweetheart Elva, a delicate beauty, and politely asked about her husband, Elmo Quisite. "That brawny bozo? We're divorced," Elva said. "Now I'm ex-Quisite." A year later, Hoop published his collection of poems titled *Exquisite Elva*.

AN EXQUISITE STORY

A pile of poetry by H. H. Hoop

Exercise D: *If...*

Write the Word that best completes each sentence.

21. If the pudding tastes good, but you don't like the lumps in it, you dislike the pudding's . . . . _____

22. If Mary tells you Al got in trouble, but you didn't see Al get in trouble and Al didn't tell you himself, the news is . . . . _____

23. If you like privacy and don't want people to be able to see into your room, you would want curtains made of material that is . . . . . _____

24. If you were 12 and your brother were 22, the difference in your ages would be one . . . . _____

25. If you're proud of your report card and want to show it off, you might present it to your parents by waving it before them with a . . . _____

26. If you are always disagreeing with people, hardly ever smile, and growl when someone says hello, you are . . . . _____

27. If your lunch is a boring sandwich that fills you up but is not what you'd call great, you might describe it as . . . . _____

Quick LIST

adequate ADJ.
agony N.
audible ADJ.
brawny ADJ.
cantankerous ADJ.
decade N.
exquisite ADJ.
ferocious ADJ.
flourish N., V.
hearsay N.
impartial ADJ.
mar V.
opaque ADJ.
ransack V.
texture N.

Exercise E: Synonyms

Write the Word that is closest in meaning to each set of words and phrases.

28. torment; torture

    _____

29. wild; brutal; merciless

    _____

30. dent; chip; scar; mark

    _____

31. satisfactory; not too bad

    _____

32. cranky; grouchy; grumpy

    _____

33. gorgeous; graceful; beautiful

    _____

34. sturdy; rugged; strong as an ox

    _____

35. look high and low; turn upside down

    _____

Exercise F: Fill-in

Write the Word that best completes each sentence. Use each word only once.

36. It is important for teachers to be _____ so that one student doesn't feel more favored than another.

37. Football players are usually either fast or _____, and some of them are both.

38. My aunt has the most _____ set of china that she washes and dries by hand for fear of damaging it.

39. The scar on Karen's forehead does not _____ her beauty; it just makes her look more interesting.

40. A dog whistle makes a special noise that is not _____ to people, but dogs can hear it for blocks.

41. It takes more than a _____ to complete your regular schooling, and many people then go on to four years of college.

42. The _____ around school is that Mr. Bowen is quitting after this year, but I want to ask him myself if it's true.

43. Did a burglar _____ your room looking for something, or do you always leave it this messy?

44. We used to have a _____ neighbor who was very hard to get along with, and he always made me nervous.

45. Lions and tigers are _____ animals, but bears can be just as dangerous.

46. I've been hurt many times, but I've never felt real _____, and I hope I never will!

47. Children need good food, exercise, and love in order to _____.

48. The _____ of brick gives the wall an interesting, rough look.

49. We will need a lot of food to have a meal that is _____ for twelve hungry people.

50. Since aluminum foil is _____, if you wrap food with it, you can't see what's inside.

A CANTANKEROUS STORY

In 1965, 86-year-old Clyde Cloop of Cantanker County, Kentucky, complained to local police that someone was following him around and wouldn't stop whistling at him. Cloop said the sound was audible wherever he went, causing him great agony. "Oh, for crying out loud," Cloop's wife Clara told the policeman, "Clyde is just an old Cantanker-ous man, and he refuses to get his hearing aid fixed!"

A Cantanker County cop (who needs an aspirin)

Lesson 13

belated *bih•LAY•tud* ADJECTIVE

too late; not on time [I missed the first act of the play because of my *belated* arrival.]

caress *kuh•RES*

VERB to stroke tenderly or lovingly [Mothers often *caress* their children to soothe them.]

NOUN a tender or loving touch [I gave the cat a *caress* as she walked past.]

convey *kun•VAY* VERB

1. to carry or transport [Many pioneers used covered wagons to *convey* their possessions and supplies.]

2. to make known; to communicate [I sent a card to *convey* my sympathy.]

exclude *ex•KLOOD* VERB

to keep out; to shut out [I'll invite the whole class because I don't want to *exclude* anyone.]

fluster *FLUS•tur* VERB

to make or become nervous and unsure [Don't let the fans' cheering *fluster* you; just concentrate on making the shot.]

frayed *FRADE* ADJECTIVE

worn thin at the edges, ragged [The collar on that old shirt is *frayed*.]

fundamental *fun•duh•MEN•tul*

ADJECTIVE basic; essential; necessary [Food is a *fundamental* need for all living things.]

NOUN something that is basic or essential; a necessity [In basketball, dribbling is a *fundamental*.]

glade *GLADE* NOUN

a grassy open space in a forest [We picnicked in the *glade*.]

illusion *ih•LOO•zhun* NOUN

1. a misleading appearance [Mirrors can create the *illusion* that a small room is big.]

2. a false idea or mistaken belief [My *illusion* that I didn't need to study was ruined by an F.]

incentive *in•SEN•tuv* NOUN

something that makes one take action or cause sone to work harder [My *incentive* for mowing the lawn was the payment that my dad offered me.]

remote *rih•MOTE* ADJECTIVE

1. far off in place or time; not near or recent [He has a *remote* cabin in the woods.]

2. slight or faint [There is only a *remote* possibility that we'll win.]

skimp *SKIMP* VERB

to spend or use as little as possible [If I really *skimp*, I can make this money last all week.]

strive *STRIVE* VERB

to try hard; to make great efforts [We will *strive* to do our best.]

torso *TOR•so* NOUN

the human body, not including the arms, legs, and head; trunk [Twist your *torso* to the left.]

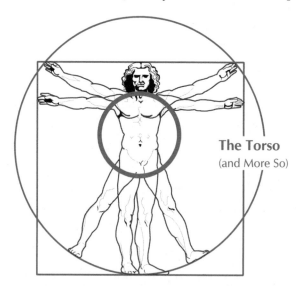

The Torso
(and More So)

venomous *VEN•uh•mus* ADJECTIVE

1. poisonous [Honeybees are *venomous*, which is why a bee sting swells and hurts.]

2. hateful; evil; showing ill will [When I proved that Lisa was lying, she gave me a *venomous* look.]

Exercise A: Put It Briefly

Write the Word that best completes each sentence.

1. People don't jog unless they want to become stronger or lose
   weight or get in shape or increase their energy. *Briefly*, they
   need some sort of . . . .   _____

2. School started at 8:00 but I didn't get there until 8:30, which
   was later than I was supposed to be there, so I was tardy. *Briefly*,
   my arrival was . . . .   _____

3. Lena got sunburned on her face and arms and neck and legs
   and everywhere except what was protected by her swimming
   suit. *Briefly*, what doesn't hurt is her . . . .   _____

4. If that spider bites you, you'll swell up and hurt and itch because
   it will inject this stuff that's harmful to your body and can be
   very dangerous. *Briefly*, that spider is . . . .   _____

5. Those pants cuffs look shabby because, though they're not torn,
   the material is all worn away due to rubbing on the ground.
   Briefly, the cuffs are . . . .   _____

6. That cow doesn't really have twice as many legs as it should; it's two
   cows, with one partly hidden behind the other. *Briefly*, that eight-
   legged cow is an . . . .   _____

Exercise B: Yes or No

Circle YES or NO for each question.

7. Is a fire **venomous**? . . . .   YES   NO

8. Is your chin part of your **torso**? . . . . .   YES   NO

9. Do most valentines **convey** affection? . . .   YES   NO

10. Does a window screen **exclude** breezes? . . . . .   YES   NO

11. Does a magician's act depend on **illusions**? . . . . . .   YES   NO

12. Would a reward often work as an **incentive**? . . . .   YES   NO

13. Would you be likely to see a skyscraper in a **glade**? . . . .   YES   NO

14. Is multiplication a **fundamental** part of mathematics? . . . .   YES   NO

15. Are your chances of being struck by lightning **remote**? . . . .   YES   NO

16. Would it **fluster** a singer to forget a song during a performance? . . . .   YES   NO

Question:
Why was Cinderella
excluded from the
basketball team?

Answer
Because she ran
away from the ball and
then lost her shoe.

Exercise C: Synonyms

Write the **Word** that is a synonym for each of these words.

17. attempt   _____

18. tardy   _____

19. disturb   _____

20. pat   _____

21. clearing   _____

Exercise D: Rhyme Time

Write the **Word** that best completes each rhyme.

22. A faraway canoe is a _____ boat.

23. To cuddle Elizabeth is to _____ Bess.

24. To struggle not to die is to _____ to survive.

25. To leave one fellow out is to _____ a dude.

26. To serve very few shellfish is to _____ on the shrimp.

27. To haul horse food elsewhere is to _____ hay away.

28. A ragged covering on a window is a _____ shade.

Exercise E: Antonyms

Write the **Word** that is an antonym for each set of words.

29. kind; warm-hearted; tender   _____

30. take it easy; quit; give up   _____

31. include; contain; take in   _____

32. nearby; close; not far   _____

33. waste; spend; use up   _____

34. extra; unimportant   _____

35. reality; truth; fact   _____

Words to Go!

Exercise F

Exercise F: Fill-in

Write the Word that best completes each sentence.
Use each word only once.

36. One has to have a very flexible _____ to do a back bend.

37. The old tablecloth was _____ and faded from years of use.

38. Reading, writing, and arithmetic are _____ parts of education.

39. His grandfather's _____ helped to calm the frightened little boy.

40. If you _____ on the sugar, your homemade lemonade will be too sour.

41. A saying that urges one to continue to _____ is "If at first you don't succeed, try, try again."

42. A large van will be used to _____ the team and all the equipment to the tournament.

43. The ship reached the _____ island after weeks of sailing.

44. My _____ that I was the team's best hitter was destroyed when I struck out nine times in a row.

45. A lovely _____ provided a nice resting place after our long hike in the woods.

46. Many organizations that used to _____ women now allow them to join.

47. I'm sure it would _____ me to drop my note cards in the middle of giving a speech.

48. A water moccasin is not a shoe; it's a _____ snake that should be avoided.

49. Our _____ to get our work done quickly was Dad's promise of a trip to the beach.

50. We sent her a _____ birthday card two weeks after her birthday.

Quick LIST

Quick LIST

belated ADJ.
caress V., N.
convey V.
exclude V.
fluster V.
frayed ADJ.
fundamental ADJ., N.
glade N.
illusion N.
incentive N.
remote ADJ.
skimp V.
strive V.
torso N.
venomous ADJ.

Are You Sure About Your Eyes?

In this optical illusion, is the dot *inside* the box or *outside* it?

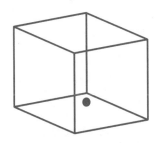

Answer: If you can't see this one, just keep trying. At first the dot will seem to be outside (or inside) the box; then when you look again, it's the opposite. The dot appears to move as your eyes focus and re-focus. They're trying to make this illusion make sense!

Lesson 14

abide *uh•BIDE* VERB

    1. to bear patiently; to put up with [I cannot *abide* loud music.]

    2. to last; to stay or remain [The young couple thought their love would *abide* forever.]

    3. to accept; to obey or follow; to remain faithful to (used with *by*) [We must *abide* by the rules.]

access *AK•ses* NOUN

    1. an approach or way to a place [The only *access* is by water.]

    2. the ability or permission to approach, enter, or use [The Internet provides *access* to a great deal of information.]

chaos *KAY•os* NOUN

extreme confusion and disorder [Five kids playing in a room can quickly create *chaos*.]

erect *ih•REKT*

ADJECTIVE straight up and down [I leaned against the wall, too tired to stand *erect*.]

VERB to build [They will *erect* a tower here.]

Question:

If it took *three* farmhands one week to erect a barn, how long would it take *six* farmhands?

Answer
No time at all, since it's already been built!

excursion *ek•SKUR•zhun* NOUN

a short trip for pleasure [We took a weekend *excursion*.]

gorge *GORJ*

NOUN a deep, narrow valley, usually steep and rocky [The trail leads through a *gorge*.]

VERB to stuff with food; to eat greedily [I always *gorge* myself when I eat at Grandma's.]

grimy *GRY•mee* ADJECTIVE

covered with dirt that has been rubbed into the surface; very dirty [Cleaning the fireplace left me *grimy*.]

inscription *in•SKRIP•shun* NOUN

    1. something carved or written on a surface, especially something meant to last [There is an *inscription* on the base of the statue.]

    2. a brief message written inside a book [The *inscription* said, "To Tom, on his twelfth birthday, with love from Grandma."]

intolerable *in•TOL•ur•uh•bul* ADJECTIVE

too hard or painful to stand; unbearable [The heat on the desert was *intolerable*.]

pulverize *PUL•vur•ize* VERB

    1. to crush or grind into powder or dust [This machine will *pulverize* the stone.]

    2. to destroy completely [The bomb will *pulverize* the target.]

qualm *KWOM* or *KWOLM* NOUN

    1. a doubt or uncertainty; uneasiness (often plural) [I have *qualms* about tomorrow's test.]

    2. a guilty feeling (often plural) [She is so dishonest, she tells lies without a *qualm*.]

robust *roh•BUST* ADJECTIVE

strong and healthy [The *robust* children ran and played.]

taut *TAWT* ADJECTIVE

stretched firmly; drawn tight [Keep the rope *taut* so it doesn't sag.]

throng *THRONG*

NOUN a large gathering; a crowd [The *throng* jammed the room.]

VERB to crowd together; to crowd into [For the championship game, thousands of fans will *throng* the gym.]

tranquil *TRAN•kwul* ADJECTIVE

calm; quiet; peaceful [We spent a *tranquil* hour gazing at the clouds.]

Exercise A: What Is It?

Write the Word that each clue describes.

Stealing dirt is
this kind of crime.   _____

1. Fences, walls, and locked gates and doors prevent this.   _____

2. If a teacher ever left a kindergarten class alone for half an hour, this is probably what she'd find when she returned.   _____

3. In this, you may get bumped and shoved, but so will everyone else you're shoulder-to-shoulder with.   _____

4. If a redwood is a good example of a tree, then the Grand Canyon is a good example of this.   _____

5. This makes you hesitate about doing something you think is wrong or dangerous.   _____

6. A suitcase might be useful for this, but a briefcase should be left at home.   _____

7. This could be a set of initials on the handles of silverware or the words "Public Library" carved in stone above a door.   _____

Exercise B: True or False

Circle TRUE or FALSE for each statement.

Beautiful canyons are simply *gorges*!	TRUE	FALSE
8. An ***inscription*** on a statue of a hero usually gives the person's name.	TRUE	FALSE
9. If you ***gorge*** yourself, you feel extremely full.	TRUE	FALSE
10. People usually dread going on an ***excursion***.	TRUE	FALSE
11. To make flour from wheat, one must ***pulverize*** the grain.	TRUE	FALSE
12. A feeling of great confidence is called a ***qualm***.	TRUE	FALSE
13. If you are very relaxed, your muscles feel ***taut***.	TRUE	FALSE
14. After a day without drinking, your thirst would be ***intolerable***.	TRUE	FALSE

Exercise C: Rhyme Time

Write the Word that completes each rhyme.
This exercise continues on the next page.

If Sis sees a mouse,
It's ___ in our house!   _____

15. As I climbed up the ladder, I was calm.
    Then I looked down (and down) and felt a ___ .   _____

16. The fence isn't finished. The last time I checked it,
    The workers had barely begun to ___ it.   _____

17. Eat right and get some exercise. You see, you really must
    If you expect to grow up strong and healthy and ___.

    _____

18. "You're out!" the umpire said to me, despite my perfect slide,
    And he makes the decisions by which players must ___.

    _____

19. The line to get the tickets is about a mile long.
    The band's so good, their audience is going to be a ___.

    _____

20. This isn't hard to understand, just use a little thought.
    A tightrope simply *isn't* one unless the rope is ___.

    _____

21. Don't use a sledge to hang a picture. Anyone who tries it
    Will ruin all the plaster, for a sledge will ___ it.

    _____

Exercise D: Antonyms

Write the Word that is an antonym for each set of words.

22. pleasant; bearable; comfortable   _____

23. knock down; destroy; demolish   _____

24. scatter; spread out; split up   _____

25. unhealthy; weak; delicate   _____

26. noisy; violent; disturbing   _____

27. clean; spotless; pure   _____

28. calm; neatness   _____

29. exit; way out   _____

Question:
What is the difference
between an angry, noisy
throng and a cow that has
a sore throat?

Exercise E: Writing

What do you find *intolerable*? A sore throat? Living
in a *grimy* city? Being trapped in a *throng* of people?
On your own paper, use at least THREE Words in a
paragraph describing what you find intolerable.

M-oo-uh
(Ahem!)
mm-O-ee
Oh, my!

Answer: One boos madly,
and the other moos badly.

Quick LIST

abide V.	**erect** ADJ., V.	**grimy** ADJ.	**pulverize** V.	**taut** ADJ.
access N.	**excursion** N.	**inscription** N.	**qualm** N.	**throng** N., V.
chaos N.	**gorge** N., V.	**intolerable** ADJ.	**robust** ADJ.	**tranquil** ADJ.

Exercise F: Other Forms of Words

Using what you know about the Words, circle
TRUE or FALSE for each statement.

*If eight is your lucky number,
you can't toler-eight it.* . . . .   TRUE   FALSE

30. At their weddings, couples promise **abiding** love.   TRUE   FALSE

31. If the lions' cages were left open, a zoo would become **chaotic**. . . . .   TRUE   FALSE

32. After it snows, people shovel their walks to make their houses **accessible**. . . . . .   TRUE   FALSE

33. A Fourth of July celebration is usually a scene of great **tranquillity**. . . . .   TRUE   FALSE

34. An identification bracelet has the owner's name **inscribed** on it. . . . .   TRUE   FALSE

35. Good housekeepers like to see **grime** in their homes.   TRUE   FALSE

Exercise G: Fill-in

Write the Word that best completes each
sentence. Use each word only once.

*If you hate a certain hive, you can't
_____ that bees' abode.*

36. I know I did the right thing, so I don't have a single _____ about my actions.

37. Excuse the _____; my six cousins are visiting, and the dog just had puppies!

38. The house was _____ while the children were napping, but not afterwards!

39. Our parents can't _____ fighting in the car, so Janie and I try to get along.

40. The conditions in the prison camp were _____, and many prisoners died.

41. At the bottom of the _____, there is a river where people take raft trips.

42. The _____ on the memorial honors the soldiers who fought in the war.

43. Put screens on your windows, or flies will have _____ to your house.

44. We went on a short _____ since we didn't have time for a long trip.

45. My jeans were _____ after I'd spent the day working in the garden.

46. On New Year's Eve, a _____ gathers in Times Square to celebrate.

47. My old dog is _____ enough to keep up with dogs half her age.

48. An elephant's ears hang down, but a horse's ears are _____.

49. My dog's leash was _____ as he pulled me down the street.

50. If a car runs over a pair of glasses, it will _____ them.

MU ee-ee nnnuu mmmoo Oh. MOOOO!

Lesson 15 _____

aspire *uh•SPIRE* VERB

to have an ambition for something; to desire earnestly or strive for a goal   [I *aspire* to be a lawyer.]

coordinated *koh•OR•duh•nay•tud* ADJECTIVE

1. arranged in proper order; working well together, as of parts   [We'll succeed in getting this done only if our efforts are *coordinated*.]
2. smoothly adjusted, as of muscles in producing difficult movements; not clumsy [A good dancer moves in a *coordinated* way.]

ignoramus *ig•nuh•RAY•mus* NOUN

one who knows nothing; an ignorant person [I'm a math whiz but a poetry *ignoramus*.]

melodious *mel•OH•dee•us* ADJECTIVE

sweet-sounding; pleasing to the ear; musical [That *melodious* sound is the song of a wren.]

merge *MURJ* VERB

to swallow up, absorb or combine, or to become absorbed in something else   [Drivers need to be careful when they *merge* into the traffic on a highway.]

motive *MOH•tuv* NOUN

a thought, need, or feeling that makes a person act   [Chuck's main *motive* for joining the team was to make new friends, not to play baseball.]

necessitate *nuh•SES•uh•tate* VERB

to make necessary   [Breaking your leg will *necessitate* the use of crutches.]

passionate *PASH•un•ut* ADJECTIVE

1. having very strong feelings; enthusiastic [The people in that family are certainly a very *passionate* group.]
2. very strong; intense   [He has a *passionate* desire to succeed.]

piteous *PIT•ee•us* ADJECTIVE

causing a feeling of pity; pitiful   [The hungry kids in the news photos were a *piteous* sight.]

quibble *KWIB•bul* VERB

to argue over an unimportant matter   [Ron and Don constantly *quibble* about things like who should turn off the light.]

random *RAN•dum* ADJECTIVE

with no particular order or pattern; made or done without a careful choice or plan   [Each child will select a gift in a *random* fashion by reaching into the grab bag.]

rapture *RAP•chur* NOUN

very great joy   [The beautiful music filled me with *rapture*.]

repentance *ruh•PEN•tuns* NOUN

sorrow for doing wrong   [After Mona hurt my feelings, she tried to show her *repentance* by being really nice.]

sever *SEV•ur* VERB

to cut apart or separate   [We used a knife to *sever* the rope.]

ultimate *UL•tuh•mit* ADJECTIVE

1. last or final, especially describing that which comes at the end   [We worked too quickly and used poor materials, and the *ultimate* result was that our clubhouse fell down.]
2. greatest or highest possible   [What is the *ultimate* speed at which this plane can fly?]

"This is Mary Sue Moss at Ultimate Shopping Center in beautiful Foggybottom. Today we're talking to random

folks here at the mall. We want to hear what local shoppers feel truly passionate about. But first we have a few words from our sponsors. So stay tuned!"

Exercise A: Yes or No

Circle YES or NO for each statement.

1. Are you asking about a **motive** if you say, "Why did you do that?" . . . . YES NO

2. Have humans traveled to the **ultimate** limits of outer space? . . . . YES NO

3. Does going to school **necessitate** getting out of bed? . . . YES NO

4. Would something **piteous** make you giggle? . . . YES NO

5. Do **passionate** fans cheer a lot? . . . . . YES NO

Exercise B: Synonyms

Write the Word that is a synonym for each set of words.

6. disagree; fuss; squabble _____

7. intention; purpose; reason _____

8. upsetting; heartbreaking; sad _____

9. fool; idiot; blockhead; moron _____

10. blend; join; mingle; mix; unite _____

11. by chance; unplanned; disorganized _____

12. attempt; hope; try; hope; wish _____

13. cause; demand; force; require _____

14. regret; guilt; remorse; shame _____

15. disconnect; split; slash _____

"Don't look piteous! Be your prettiest! At **Moe's Beauty Barn**!"

"If you aspire to acquire a tire, go to **Ike's Bikes**, where the air is free!"

"These **Super Scissors** can sever whatever!"

Exercise C: Analogies

Write the letter of the word that completes the analogy.

_____ 16. **passionate** : cold :: tall :
   A. big C. heavy
   B. short D. straight

_____ 17. gymnast : **coordinated** :: judge :
   A. fair C. charming
   B. old D. talkative

_____ 18. apology : **repentance** :: laugh :
   A. giggle C. boredom
   B. sorrow D. amusement

_____ 19. happiness : **rapture** :: pain :
   A. comfort C. discomfort
   B. torture D. irritability

Exercise D: *If . . .*

Write the **Word** that best completes each sentence.

20. If your pants and shirt look good together, your socks match, and you're wearing shoes that go with your clothes, your outfit is . . . . . _____

21. If you think that a certain bike is the fanciest, fastest, safest, and best looking; if it's just "the tops," you'd say that bike was the . . . . . _____

22. If you saw a harmless animal caught in a trap and having no success in trying to get free, you would probably think its struggles were . . . _____

23. If your team has too few players and joins with another small team to make a bigger one, what the two teams do is to . . . . _____

24. If you disagree with someone about everything and can't ignore it when he or she is wrong about some detail, you two tend to . . . . _____

Exercise E: *Other Forms of Words*

Use what you know about the **Words** to choose the correct answers.

_____ 25. An employee might get *severance* pay when he or she
A. is fired.   B. starts a job.   C. works overtime.

_____ 26. One thing that makes noise *melodiously* is a
A. siren.   B. jet.   C. songbird.

_____ 27. A person with an *aspiration* is often said to have
A. a dream.   B. a problem.   C. an assignment.

_____ 28. What is something that people often select *randomly*?
A. a spouse   B. a pet   C. a sack of potatoes

_____ 29. Someone who feels *rapturous* might make the sound
A. "Ouch!"   B. "Ugh!"   C. "Ahhhh!"

Exercise F: *Antonyms*

Write the **Word** that is an antonym for each underlined word.
This exercise continues on the next page.

30. When my best friend moved away, I cried with <u>misery</u>; when I heard she was moving back, I sighed with ___. _____

31. The saleswoman made a <u>beginning</u> offer of a price for the new car; after an hour of bargaining, she gave her ___ offer. _____

32. I might look at a book of stories and make a <u>deliberate</u> choice, or I might read whatever story the book opens to, which is ___. _____

And now *these* words from our

Quick LIST

aspire V.
coordinated ADJ.
ignoramus N.
melodious ADJ.
merge V.
motive N.
necessitate V.
passionate ADJ.
piteous ADJ.
quibble V.
random ADJ.
rapture N.
repentance N.
sever V.
ultimate ADJ.

33. Some people's voices are harsh and screeching and <u>unpleasant</u>; others' voices are quite ___.

_____

34. When I got 100 on the history quiz, I felt like a <u>genius</u>; when I spelled *brain* wrong, I felt like a total ___.

_____

35. Some people show little emotion and seem <u>unfeeling</u>; others have fierce loves and hates and seem quite ___.

_____

Exercise G: Fill-in

Write the Word that best completes each sentence. Use each word only once.

36. Mom said if she heard my sister and me _____ about whose turn it was to sit in the front seat, she'd let the dog sit there.

37. A _____ desire for independence from England led some colonists to form a group called the Sons of Liberty.

38. We mustn't forget those soldiers who made the _____ sacrifice in fighting for America—those who paid with their lives.

39. The _____ I felt when the rocket I had built shot 200 feet straight up was one of the happiest times I had growing up.

40. Having twenty guests for Thanksgiving will _____ using card tables to seat some of the people.

41. I felt like a real _____ when I realized that I'd shrunk all my sweaters by washing them in hot water.

42. Sherry's movements were so perfectly _____ that she was able to dodge the other player, turn, dribble, and score.

43. Your shovel might _____ the roots if you are not very careful while digging up that plant.

44. Detectives try to learn what someone's _____ might have been for committing a crime.

45. Because I _____ to be a veterinarian, I want to take a lot of biology courses in high school.

46. It's hard to forgive someone who shows no _____ for what he or she has done.

47. The _____ cries of the frightened child made me hurry to his side to find out what was wrong.

48. My choice of which socks to wear is _____; I just grab the first pair I can lay my hands on.

49. Two classes will _____ into one group for the trip.

50. I think that chirping crickets make a _____ sound.

"Need a better trap? For me, **Rat Capture** means cat rapture!"

"Even if you're famous, You're just an ignoramus If you don't shop! shop! shop! at **Amos**!"

"And now back to Mary Sue Moss . . ."

Word Fun 3! _____

Puzzling

Identify the **Word** from Unit 3 that fits the clue in each box.
The word's first letter is shown in the answer blank.

	leave out

1. e _____

6. g _____

| YEAR   YEAR |
| YEAR   YEAR |
| YEAR   YEAR |
| YEAR   YEAR |
| YEAR   YEAR |

2. d _____

TI NOT ME

7. b _____

| C O U |
| N S N |
| I O F |

3. c _____

IN C IV

8. i _____

CU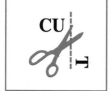

4. s _____

S
T
A
N
D

9. e _____

MISTAKE

5. b _____

BASIC

10. f _____

Searching

Circle all the words you can find that go from left to right or from top to bottom in the puzzle. Among them, you should find the answers to all of these clues.

1. A *robust* person is this.
2. This is one kind of *caress*.
3. This describes an *impartial* person.
4. You do this when you *devour* something.
5. *Illiteracy* involves the inability to do this.
6. Rolling around in this makes you *grimy*.
7. This is a synonym for *rapture*.
8. This would *mar* a car.

B	O	F	I	J	O	Y
R	E	A	D	E	H	U
O	A	I	O	M	U	D
S	T	R	O	N	G	E
E	N	D	R	I	K	N
L	S	O	A	P	O	T

Naming

Match each person's name to the description it goes best with.

____ 1. Ken Tankerus   A. She casts a spell.

____ 2. Mel O. Dias   B. She blocks the light.

____ 3. Dee Vower   C. She eats like a horse.

____ 4. Cal Amitty   D. He gets people going.

____ 5. Moe Tuvv   E. He can sing like a bird.

____ 6. Tex Churr   F. He is really big trouble.

____ 7. N. Chant   G. She's truly a confused mess.

____ 8. Kay Oss   H. He's grumpy and hard to deal with.

____ 9. O. Pake   I. He's judged by his surface qualities.

Ken   Mel

Dee

Defining

Match the invented word with its meaning.

____ 1. nagony   A. what you call something when there's enough of it but it's awful

____ 2. audibull   B. what you call a chicken that's been hypnotized

____ 3. furocious   C. the pain an old, broken-down horse feels

____ 4. excarsion   D. what is written on a torn bit of paper

____ 5. badequate   E. a calf's dad when he sneezes loudly

____ 6. inscraption   F. an uneducated, deer-like animal

____ 7. venomouse   G. a fun trip in an automobile

____ 8. henchanted   H. a mean, dangerous mink

____ 9. ignoramoose   I. a poisonous rodent

"Excuse me."

Rhyming

These poems would be better if they rhymed. Substitute a **Word** from Unit 3 for each underlined word or phrase to make the line rhyme with the one above it.

1. "I'm so sorry I did that" is quite a good sentence
   To use when you're trying to show your <u>regret</u>.

   _____

2. To get to my house, take a plane, and then you'll need a boat;
   Then ride a mule for eighteen miles. My house is quite <u>far away</u>!

   _____

Lesson 16 _____

ally *AL•eye* NOUN

a person or nation that is on one's side [My brother and I often quarrel, but he's my *ally* if I'm really in trouble.]

analysis *uh•NAL•uh•sis* NOUN

a careful study that looks closely at a thing's parts or elements [An *analysis* of our soil showed which plants would grow well in it.]

atrocious *uh•TROH•shus* ADJECTIVE

1. extremely cruel, wicked, or brutal [*Atrocious* acts are committed in wartime.]

2. extremely bad; of very poor quality [My handwriting is *atrocious*; no one can read it.]

client *KLY•unt* NOUN

a customer; a person or group that uses professional services [Cora says it's her duty as a lawyer to help every *client* she has, even if she doesn't approve of that person.]

discord *DIS•kord* NOUN

disagreement and lack of harmony between persons, things, or ideas [Frequent *discord* on the city council made it almost impossible to get anything done.]

gourmet *gor•MAY* NOUN

a person who understands and enjoys fine food [Hal, who is a *gourmet*, loves fancy restaurants.]

lenient *LEEN•ee•unt* ADJECTIVE

not very strict [My parents insist on lights out by 9:00, but Henry's parents are more *lenient*.]

petty *PET•ee* ADJECTIVE

1. small and unimportant [Why argue about *petty* differences of opinion?]

2. having a mean or narrow outlook [Ralph's saying my shoes are ugly was a *petty* remark.]

prank *PRANK* NOUN

an act of mischief; a practical joke [Putting salt in the sugar bowl was his favorite *prank*.]

pursue *pur•SOO* VERB

1. to try to catch; to chase [The lion gave up and did not continue to *pursue* the antelope.]

2. to try for (a goal) [Some people *pursue* wealth their entire lives.]

reassure *ree•uh•SHUR* VERB

to restore confidence or peace of mind [I was able to *reassure* my parents that I was not hurt in the accident.]

tarnish *TAR•nish*

NOUN a dull coating that forms on metal when it is exposed to certain chemicals or to air over a period of time. [Silver polish is good at removing *tarnish*.]

VERB **1.** to become dull or discolored [If you don't polish brass, it will eventually *tarnish*.]

VERB **2.** to spoil the perfection of something [One mistake can *tarnish* a person's reputation.]

theory *THEER•ee* NOUN

1. an explanation based on thought; an idea for which there is some evidence and that many accept as true but has not been proven [One *theory* about why dinosaurs died off is that the climate became too cool for them to survive.]

2. an idea, belief, or opinion about something [She acted on the *theory* that children respond better to rewards than to punishments.]

vain *VAIN* ADJECTIVE

1. showing too much pride in one's abilities or appearance [Pete is so *vain* that he can't pass a mirror without looking at himself.]

2. with little or no result; not successful [We made a *vain* attempt to catch the bus.]

vigorous *VIG•ur•us* ADJECTIVE

1. full of strength or energy, physically or mentally [You need to be a *vigorous* person to work on a farm.]

2. requiring strength and energy [Chopping wood is a *vigorous* activity.]

Exercise A: Rhyme Time
Write the Word that best completes each rhyme.

1. A monster who's nasty and truly ferocious
   Might well take some actions that we'd call ___.

   _____

2. Mean, nasty comments can fly like confetti
   When people give in to the urge to be ___.

   _____

3. I was scared of being sick and begged a doc to cure me.
   "You'll be fine tomorrow," said the doc to ___ me.

   _____

4. An ostrich has an itsy-bitsy, teeny-tiny brain.
   Don't try to teach one tricks because your efforts will be ___.

   _____

5. Lack of sleep will make you weary.
   That's proven; it is not a ___.

   _____

6. As long as there's ketchup, then dinner's okay.
   I guess I don't qualify as a ___.

   _____

7. Mom thought the dryer broke because she heard it bang and clank.
   Phil put a pot in with the clothes; he loves that sort of ___.

   _____

It's a Theory

Professor Norbert Allen Schloopenhoopendorf recently said the Earth's core is filled with blueberry cream pie.

When asked if he had any evidence to support this unusual idea, the professor replied vigorously, "What else could it be? Lemon pudding?"

Exercise B: Synonyms
Write the Word that is a synonym for each set of words.

8. stuck-up; conceited; proud

   _____

9. shocking; monstrous; disgusting

   _____

10. follow; run after; hunt; track

   _____

11. strong; active; full of energy

   _____

12. minor; trivial; unimportant

   _____

13. partner; assistant; helper

   _____

14. trick; gag; monkeyshine

   _____

15. clash; arguing; conflict

   _____

16. soil; stain; smear; damage

   _____

17. buyer; consumer; user; purchaser

   _____

18. investigation; examination; inspection

   _____

19. easy-going; mild; flexible; permissive

   _____

Exercise C: Other Forms of Words

Use what you know about the **Words** to choose the correct answers.

____ 20. One type of **alliance** is a
A. team.　　　　B. umpire.　　　　C. uniform.

____ 21. Another name for a **prankster** is a
A. bully.　　　　B. criminal.　　　　C. practical joker.

____ 22. A person might show his or her **vigor** by
A. telling jokes.　　B. writing poems.　　C. doing exercises.

____ 23. A store's **clientele** *[kly•un•TEL]* are the people who
A. work there.　　B. shop there.　　C. own the store.

____ 24. You might call a statue an **atrocity** if you thought it was
A. very ugly.　　B. expensive.　　C. breakable.

Exercise D: If . . .

Write the **Word** that best completes each sentence.

25. If the teacher lets you get by with turning in homework late
and skipping tests, she is too . . . . _____

26. If a silver spoon looks kind of gray or even black instead of
shiny, you could make it pretty again by getting rid of the . . . . _____

27. If your doctor sends a lab some of your blood to make sure it
contains enough red cells, what the lab does is an . . . . _____

28. If you wonder how the dog got out of the yard and then find loose
boards in the fence, your idea about his escape would be a . . . . . . _____

29. If you like only the finest foods, enjoy eating unusual things, and
know which chefs work at which restaurants, you are a . . . . _____

Exercise E: Antonyms

Write the **Word** that is an antonym for each set of words.
This exercise continues on the next page.

But They're
My Clients
_____

Why did the
vet have to
change careers?

Answer: She was allergic to her clients.

30. frighten; upset; worry _____

31. weak; tired; lazy _____

32. enemy; opponent _____

33. harmony; agreement _____

Quick LIST

ally　N.
analysis　N.
atrocious　ADJ.
client　N.
discord　N.
gourmet　N.
lenient　ADJ.
petty　ADJ.
prank　N.
pursue　V.
reassure　V.
tarnish　N., V.
theory　N.
vain　ADJ.
vigorous　ADJ.

34. flee; run away; escape _____

35. useful; effective; productive _____

Exercise F: Fill-in

Write the Word that best completes each sentence. Use each word only once.

36. You may very well be the victim of a _____ on April Fool's Day.

37. Sonja talked forever, giving us every _____ detail about her day.

38. Let's see whether the facts support your _____ about how the fire started.

39. The United States was an important _____ of England during World War II.

40. As soon as the _____ of the victim's leftover coffee has been completed, we will know if it contained poison.

41. My grandparents are more _____ about what I can and can't do than my parents are.

42. When I saw that they were fearful, I tried to _____ our new neighbors that our dog doesn't bite.

43. I made several _____ efforts to catch my parakeet but then he flew back in his cage by himself.

44. How dare you try to _____ my good name by saying that I am a thief?

45. Lee's lessons and constant practicing help him _____ success as a musician.

46. My great-grandmother is still _____ enough to walk a mile every day.

47. Even Mr. Clark, who is quite a _____, says that Mom's peach pie is the best dessert he's ever tasted.

48. The show was absolutely _____ because the performers had no talent at all.

49. If my sister and I had separate rooms, there would be less _____ in our house.

50. Mom's in a good mood because a _____ of hers said that he was really pleased with her work.

Lesson 17

collaborate *kuh•LAB•uh•rate* VERB
to work together to get something done, such as a work of art, literature, or science [Mark and Celia will *collaborate* on a project for the History Fair.]

contempt *kun•TEMPT* NOUN
scorn; a feeling that someone or something is worthless [I feel *contempt* for people who steal.]

corrupt *kuh•RUPT*
VERB to change something that should be good or honest into something bad [Bribes can be used to *corrupt* public officials.]
ADJECTIVE dishonest; wicked [There are very few *corrupt* judges in our country.]

delusion *dih•LOO•zhun* NOUN
a false belief [Although Hank isn't very good at all, he has the *delusion* that he's the best player on the team.]

efficient *ih•FISH•unt* ADJECTIVE
achieving the best results with the least waste of time or energy; capable [The police have found that using bicycles is an *efficient* way to patrol large parks.]

eloquent *EL•uh•kwunt* ADJECTIVE
able to speak or write well, expressing thoughts and feelings effectively [Senator Jordan was so *eloquent* that audiences laughed, cried, and cheered when they heard her.]

essential *uh•SEN•shul* ADJECTIVE
of the greatest importance; necessary [Inviting guests who get along with each other is *essential* to the success of a party.]

fortify *FOR•tuh•fy* VERB
to make stronger or more effective [Many manufacturers *fortify* cereal with vitamins.]

involuntary *in•VOL•un•tair•ee* ADJECTIVE
done without choice or control [Hiccuping is an *involuntary* action.]

morale *muh•RAL* NOUN
the attitude that reflects the degree of enthusiasm, confidence, or bravery [Team *morale* was high for the championship game.]

pathetic *puh•THET•ik* ADJECTIVE
causing one to feel pity [The cat looked *pathetic* with her tail caught in the fence.]

prolong *pruh•LONG* VERB
to make longer in time [We were having such a good time on our camping trip that we decided to *prolong* it by two days.]

provocation *prov•uh•KAY•shun* NOUN
a cause for a reaction, especially a cause for irritation or anger [If you feel grouchy, a slight *provocation* can make you snap at someone.]

resent *rih•ZENT* VERB
to feel annoyed or angry about [I *resent* your suggestion that I don't know anything about soccer.]

shrewd *SHROOD* ADJECTIVE
clever about practical things [Be careful when you bargain with Fred; he's very *shrewd*.]

My Camping Trip, Part 1

I had looked forward to the family camping trip at Crooked Creek State Park. My morale dropped when Dad said that my brother and I had to share a tent *and* to collaborate in setting it up! We did it fairly efficiently, but the tent was a little shaky. My brother "fortified" it with a stick. That worked for about twelve minutes.

Exercise A: Antonyms

Write the Word that is an antonym for each of these words and phrases.

1. admiration _____

2. pure _____

3. weaken _____

4. shorten _____

5. wasteful _____

6. foolish _____

7. by choice _____

8. unnecessary _____

9. appreciate _____

10. work independently _____

Exercise B: Yes or No

Circle YES or NO for each question.

11. When someone makes you doubt yourself, does that increase your **morale**? . . .   YES   NO

12. When people thought the earth was flat, was that a **delusion**? . . . .   YES   NO

13. Would an **eloquent** speaker hold your interest? . . . .   YES   NO

14. Is it **essential** to have six pairs of gym shoes? . . . .   YES   NO

15. Would steel rods **fortify** a wooden fence? . . . .   YES   NO

16. Do time-outs **prolong** a basketball game? . . . .   YES   NO

17. Would a sleeping tiger be **pathetic**? . . . .   YES   NO

18. Do you **resent** a generous act? . . . .   YES   NO

My brother claimed that the moon is made of green cheese. "That is a delusion," I said. "Anyone can see that it's blue cheese!"

Exercise C: Other Forms of Words

Use what you know about the Words to choose the correct answers.

_____ 19. Which of these would you feel **contemptuous** of?
A. a cheater   B. a genius   C. a hero

_____ 20. What should the legal system do when it finds **corruption**?
A. reward it   B. support it   C. punish it

_____ 21. Who needs **eloquence** the most?
A. a librarian   B. a writer   C. a sprinter

_____ 22. Which of these would you probably feel **resentment** about?
A. a suggestion   B. a compliment   C. an insult

_____ 23. When you **provoke** someone on purpose, which is the likely response?
A. joy   B. anger   C. disbelief

Exercise D: *If . . .*

Write the Word that best completes each sentence.

24. If you believe you are from outer space and will return to your planet on your next birthday, you are suffering from a . . . .   _____

25. If you could get all your homework done, clean your room, and still have time to play before dinner, you would be . . . .   _____

26. If you always found the best price, got the best deal, and came out on top in any trade you made, you would be . . . .   _____

27. If you could use the right words in any situation and say exactly what you meant without stumbling or hesitation, you would be . . .   _____

28. If you absolutely can't get along without something, it isn't a luxury, and you just have to have it, it is . . . .   _____

29. If your brother is in a bad mood, and you know it, and you do something to "get a rise" out of him, that's a deliberate . . . .   _____

30. If you encouraged your teammates and helped everyone to feel stronger and better you would be building . . . .   _____

31. If a police officer takes money from criminals and "looks the other way" when they break the law, that officer is . . . .   _____

32. If you fell down, got dirt all over your clothes, skinned your knee, and broke your glasses, you would look . . . .   _____

33. If you were on a seesaw and the other person got off while you were up in the air, your next movement would be . . . .   _____

34. If you enjoy joining forces with someone else and working as a team to get something done, you like to . . . .   _____

35. If you made fun of someone, showed disrespect, and "looked down your nose" at him or her, you would be showing . . . .   _____

Exercise E: *Writing*

What happens to your **morale** when things don't go as you'd like? How do you **fortify** your spirits? Explain your answers on your own paper. Use at least THREE Words in your paragraph.

I always try to see the humor in things. So when Dad asked me to bait the hooks, I said, "This doesn't seem like a very *e-fish-ent* way to get a meal." Dad laughed, but I had to explain the joke to my brother.

Quick LIST

collaborate V.
contempt N.
corrupt V., ADJ.
delusion N.
efficient ADJ.
eloquent ADJ.
essential ADJ.
fortify V.
involuntary ADJ.
morale N.
pathetic ADJ.
prolong V.
provocation N.
resent V.
shrewd ADJ.

No sensible person would provoke hornets. Well, you-know-who is not very sensible. The hornets showed their contempt for him by . . . Well, I'm sure you can imagine their reaction.

Later, my brother looked really pathetic, so I gave him a granola bar. It was the one I had dropped in Crooked Creek.

Exercise F: Fill-in

Write the **Word** that best completes each sentence. Use each word only once.

36. A lost and frightened child is a _____ sight.

37. My mother insists that I _____ myself with a good breakfast every day.

38. A lot of school spirit shows that _____ at the school is high.

39. Martin Luther King, Jr., was an _____ speaker, especially in his "I Have a Dream" speech.

40. When we _____, we get to use the skills and talents of other people.

41. You won't let greed _____ you if you have strong morals.

42. I feel _____ for people who are mean to helpless animals.

43. Maude is so _____ that she gets her work done faster and better than most other people.

44. People _____ being ignored and treated as if they are unimportant.

45. Thinking you can beat me is a _____, and I'll prove it with a race.

46. Teasing the dog was the _____ that made him growl at you.

47. It is _____ for bears to eat a great deal before they hibernate for the winter.

48. Will didn't want to _____ the argument, so he gave in.

49. It was _____ of Bobby to see that the stock price would go up and to buy it while its price was low.

50. I didn't mean to yawn; it was totally _____.

Lesson 18 _____

agile *AJ•ul* ADJECTIVE

able to move quickly and easily; gracefully active   [Cats are *agile* creatures.]

antic *AN•tik* NOUN

a playful or silly act or trick (usually plural) [The puppy's *antics* are cute.]

console *kun•SOLE* VERB

to make (someone) feel less sad or disappointed; to comfort   [I tried to *console* the unhappy child by reading him a story.]

conspicuous *kun•SPIK•yoo•us* ADJECTIVE

obvious; easily seen   [The number above the door should be *conspicuous* so guests can find the house.]

falsify *FOL•suh•fy* VERB

to make something false in order to deceive [The student used a school computer to *falsify* his grade reports.]

fleet *FLEET* ADJECTIVE

swift; fast   [She is as *fleet* as a deer.]

gape *GAPE* VERB

1. to stare with the mouth wide open [Seeing my mother on stilts made me *gape* in amazement.]

2. to open wide   [Latch the gate, or it will *gape*.]

infantile *IN•fun•tile* ADJECTIVE

of or relating to infants; childish   [Her tantrum was *infantile*.]

inquisitive *in•KWIZ•uh•tiv* ADJECTIVE

1. interested in searching for truth or knowledge   [She has an *inquisitive* mind.]

2. asking too many questions about other people's business   [I was annoyed by the sales clerk's *inquisitive* remarks.]

integrity *in•TEG•ruh•tee* NOUN

moral goodness, honesty, and sincerity [A person with *integrity* does not cheat.]

maze *MAZE* NOUN

a confusing network of winding paths or passages   [He got lost in the *maze*.]

mingle *MING•gul* VERB

1. to mix together; to combine   [Toss the salad to *mingle* the ingredients.]

2. to join or participate with others   [During recess, children from different classes *mingle* on the playground.]

obligation *ob•luh•GAY•shun* NOUN

a legal or moral responsibility; that which a person must (or must not) do; duty   [It is a parent's *obligation* to protect his or her children.]

obstinate *OB•stuh•nit* ADJECTIVE

1. unreasonably determined to have one's own way; unwilling to change one's mind or do what someone else wants   [Zelda won't give in; she's too *obstinate*.]

2. hard to treat, remove, or control   [I can't get rid of this *obstinate* cold.]

ordeal *or•DEEL* NOUN

a very difficult or painful test or experience [Our long, hot hike was an *ordeal*.]

My Camping Trip, Part 2

Camping with your family can be fun. Camping with your brother can be an ordeal. Here are four things that could make camping with *your* brother more bearable.

1. A compass will help you find camp after your infantile brother takes you way out in the woods and says, "Get lost."

Exercise A: Synonyms

Write the **Word** that is closest in meaning to each set of words and phrases.

1. be all ears; itching to know; eaten up with curiosity   _____

2. plain as day; under one's nose; stick out like a sore thumb   _____

3. a real workout; a hard row to hoe; no bed of roses   _____

4. pig-headed; set in one's ways; won't give an inch   _____

5. fib; fake it; stretch the truth; cook up a story; forge   _____

6. quick as a flash; like a shot; greased lightning   _____

Exercise B: True or False

Circle TRUE or FALSE for each statement.

7. If people at a party want to get to know each other, they **mingle**. . . . .   TRUE   FALSE

8. It is a compliment to say that someone's behavior is **infantile**. . . . .   TRUE   FALSE

9. Parents usually encourage their children's **antics** at bedtime. . . . .   TRUE   FALSE

10. People who want privacy make sure their doors **gape**. . . . .   TRUE   FALSE

11. To do his or her job, a detective must be **inquisitive**. . . . .   TRUE   FALSE

12. Races are won by those who are the most **fleet**. . . . .   TRUE   FALSE

13. It is hard to find one's way out of a **maze**. . . . .   TRUE   FALSE

14. A person with **integrity** can be trusted. . . . .   TRUE   FALSE

Exercise C: Antonyms

Write the **Word** that is an antonym for each of these words.

15. slow   _____

16. upset   _____

17. mature   _____

18. hidden   _____

19. clumsy   _____

20. separate   _____

21. agreeable   _____

22. wickedness   _____

23. uninterested   _____

2. After your obstinate brother spends an hour trying to light a campfire by rubbing stones together, you can do it in a flash with an ordinary match.

Exercise D: Rhyme Time
Write the **Word** that completes each rhyme.

24. The acting was just horrid and the story was unreal.
    Sitting through that movie was a terrible ___.

    _____

25. The magician did so many tricks with hat and wand and cape
    That we were quite astonished and could only sit and ___.

    _____

26. Turn right, then left, then right twice more, and after many days,
    You *might* locate my office. Oh, this building is a ___!

    _____

27. The children will not settle down; the babysitter's frantic.
    She doesn't think that she can stand another silly ___.

    _____

28. When a tray is full of dishes that are delicate and fragile
    Don't carry it unless you're strong and also very ___.

    _____

29. "Stop whining!" said my mother. "I won't drive another mile
    With kids who both are over ten but act so ___!"

    _____

30. A fellow brought my letters. I expressed appreciation.
    "But I'm your mailman," he replied. "So it's my ___."

    _____

Exercise E: Other Forms of Words
Use what you know about the **Words** to choose the correct answers.

____ 31. When you borrow a library book, you are **obliged** to
         A. like it.   B. return it.   C. read it.

____ 32. What kind of animal is known for its **obstinance**?
         A. a mule   B. a hawk   C. a lion

____ 33. What is a word that means "a **falsified** document"?
         A. *contract*   B. *forgery*   C. *story*

____ 34. What kind of activity requires the most **agility**?
         A. weightlifting   B. gymnastics   C. fishing

____ 35. A **consolation** prize in a contest is given to a person who
         A. won.   B. didn't enter.   C. entered
                                                          but didn't win.

3. I feel an obligation to record the family's history. Do you? A camera can record all your brother's dumb antics, and photographs do not lie. (A computer, however, can help you falsify them just a bit.)

Quick LIST

agile ADJ.	**conspicuous** ADJ.	**gape** V.	**integrity** N.	**obligation** N.
antic N.	**falsify** V.	**infantile** ADJ.	**maze** N.	**obstinate** ADJ.
console V.	**fleet** ADJ.	**inquisitive** ADJ.	**mingle** V.	**ordeal** N.

Exercise F: Writing

On your own paper, write a paragraph about something that made you **gape**. Use at least THREE **Words** in your paragraph.

Wow, did my brother gape at this! I can show you the photograph.

Exercise G: Fill-in

Write the **Word** that best completes each sentence. Use each word only once.

36. We hate dealing with _____ questions from our nosy neighbor.

37. In a Greek myth, Theseus went into a _____, unrolling a ball of string behind him so he could find his way back out.

38. Each of us trusting the other's _____, we shook hands to seal our agreement.

39. Feelings of happiness and sadness can _____, producing mixed emotions.

40. Jerry is so _____ that no one can persuade him to do what he doesn't feel like doing.

41. Liz made her boredom _____ by fidgeting, yawning, and sighing.

42. Penguins are awkward on land but quite _____ in the water.

43. Traffic slowed as everyone stopped to _____ at the cars involved in the accident.

44. The judge reminded the witness of her _____ to tell the truth.

45. Joey is so _____ that he wins every race.

46. Pioneers moving west faced the _____ of crossing the mountains in wagon trains.

47. The man changed a *1* to a *4* to _____ his birth certificate.

48. It seemed that nothing could _____ the broken-hearted man.

49. Their behavior was so _____ that we were embarrassed to be seen with them.

50. The kittens amused us with one _____ after another.

4. A comfy pair of boots will make you fleet in the woods. This is good after your brother figures out where you got the compass, matches, and camera. (By the way, comfortable boots can really con-*sole* tired feet.)

Lesson 19

ascertain *as•sur•TANE* VERB
to find out for certain; to determine
[She took apart the clock to *ascertain* which part was broken.]

disclose *dis•KLOZE* VERB
to make known or public; to reveal
[The candidate decided to *disclose* the fact that he had once been arrested.]

dismay *dis•MAY*
NOUN a loss of courage or a deeply worried feeling due to being faced with trouble or danger [The farmer reacted with *dismay* to the sight of his destroyed crops.]
VERB to fill with alarm or fear [It will *dismay* Reba to find out that the test is tomorrow.]

douse *DOWCE* VERB
to plunge or push into a liquid or to pour a liquid over; to soak [A quick, mean way to wake someone is to *douse* his face with water.]

gaudy *GAW•dee* ADJECTIVE
dressed or decorated with a lot of color but very little taste [Clowns tumbled around the ring in their *gaudy* costumes.]

immune *im•YOON* ADJECTIVE
not affected by [Everyone got the flu except Flora, who seems to be *immune* to it.]

knack *NAK* NOUN
a special ability that is hard to figure out or teach [Dion has a *knack* for guessing which songs will make it big.]

negotiate *nih•GO•shee•ate* VERB
to arrange something through discussion and compromise [The principal will *negotiate* with the school board for more athletic equipment.]

plight *PLITE* NOUN
an unfortunate, difficult, or dangerous situation
[When the waves turned her boat over, May was in a terrible *plight*.]

prominent *PROM•uh•nunt* ADJECTIVE
1. sticking out; standing out [My dad has a *prominent* forehead.]
2. noticeable; easy to see [The old hotel was the most *prominent* building on the block.]
3. important and well known [Judge Keith is a *prominent* member of the community.]

ravenous *RAV•uh•nus* ADJECTIVE
very eager for food; very hungry [Kelly had skipped lunch so she was *ravenous* for dinner.]

tactics *TAK•tix* NOUN
procedures used to get an advantage or be successful; methods [Our coach always comes up with *tactics* for us to use that help us win.]

terse *TURS* ADJECTIVE
using the fewest words necessary to say something [When I asked my sister if she'd miss me, her *terse* reply was "Not much."]

urgent *UR•junt* ADJECTIVE
in need of immediate attention or action [The accident victim had an *urgent* need for a doctor.]

vessel *VES•ul* NOUN
1. a hollow container such as a cup or vase [The crystal glass was the perfect *vessel* for the deep red cranberry juice.]
2. a ship or boat [My uncle knows every *vessel* that ever anchored in that harbor.]

A Terse Conversation

Exercise A: Yes or No

Circle YES or NO for each question.

1. Do you get to have everything your way when you **negotiate**? . . . .   YES   NO
2. Do **prominent** people get more attention than most of us? . . . .   YES   NO
3. Would people be **dismayed** if their house burned down? . . . .   YES   NO
4. When people are starving, is their need for food **urgent**? . . .   YES   NO
5. If you have a **knack** for cooking, are you good at it? . . . .   YES   NO
6. Is a **plight** something people want to get into? . . . .   YES   NO
7. Do cats usually enjoy being **doused**? . . . .   YES   NO
8. Do generals use **tactics** in a battle? . . . . .   YES   NO
9. Is a normal pair of jeans **gaudy**? . . . . .   YES   NO
10. Is a dinner table a **vessel**? . . . . . .   YES   NO

A Promise
that's Terse (for
Better or Worse)

I do.

I do.

Exercise B: Opposites

Complete each sentence with a Word. To do so, you need to
know that Stan and his brother Dan are opposites in everything.

11. Stan is chatty, never gives a short answer to anything, and could talk
    your ear off, but Dan is ___.

    _____

12. Dan is a common, ordinary lawyer whom few people have ever
    heard of, but Stan is the most ___ lawyer in town.

    _____

13. Stan is always chilly and wears two sweaters and a coat all winter, but
    Dan seems ___ to the cold.

    _____

14. Dan wears gray or tan all the time, but Stan likes ___ clothing such as
    wide orange ties with bright green parrots on them.

    _____

15. Stan is all thumbs and destroys whatever he tries to repair, but Dan
    has a ___ for fixing things.

    _____

16. Dan nibbles at his food and pushes his plate away after a few bites,
    but Stan attacks every meal as if he is ___.

    _____

17. Stan loves a challenge, is never discouraged, and cannot be bullied,
    but Dan reacts to any kind of threat with ___.

    _____

18. Dan will drink only from crystal glasses or china coffee cups, but Stan
    is happy to use an old mayonnaise jar as a ___.

    _____

19. Stan has sneaky ways to get what he wants and will use any method
    he thinks will work, but Dan never uses dishonest ___.

    _____

20. Dan is relaxed and takes his time getting things done, but Stan rushes
    around thinking that every need and every job is ___.

    _____

Exercise C: Mini-Rhyme Time

Write the **Word** that best completes each rhyme.

21. A very short poem is a ___ verse. _____

22. When you take off your socks, you ___ your toes. _____

23. A truly serious problem or danger is quite a ___. _____

24. If you discover a fact and make it clear to someone, you ___ it and explain it. _____

25. Spraying water on the place you live will ___ your house. _____

26. A person who is getting a tetanus shot tomorrow will soon be ___. _____

27. If two people grab each other and struggle on a ship, they wrestle on a ___. _____

Exercise D: Synonyms

Write the **Word** that is closest in meaning to each set of words and phrases.

28. a sense of helplessness; a sinking feeling _____

29. short and to the point; with no wasted words _____

30. half-starved; could eat a horse; greedy as a pig _____

31. give and take; come to an agreement; bargain _____

32. let the cat out of the bag; spill the beans _____

33. a fix; a jam; a scrape; big trouble _____

34. know for sure; figure out _____

35. flashy; hard to miss _____

A Terse Comment on a Dairy Product

Good cheese!

When Pluto and Goofy pushed Mickey into the lake, what they did was to . . .

Joe was thrilled with his new suit and eager to . . .

If you run into a rattlesnake, you face a . . .

If you show your nervousness and fear, you . . .

A cargo ship that's loaded with bottles is a . . .

A guy with tattoos from head to toe has a . . .

A shortage of talent is a . . .

A hospital worker who doesn't have much to say is a . . .

What you would say to people who were about to get into a fight is . . .

	douse V.	**negotiate** V.	**tactics** N.
ascertain V.	**gaudy** ADJ.	**plight** N.	**terse** ADJ.
disclose V.	**immune** ADJ.	**prominent** ADJ.	**urgent** ADJ.
dismay N., V.	**knack** N.	**ravenous** ADJ.	**vessel** N.

Exercise E: Fill-in

Write the Word that best completes each sentence. Use each word only once.

douse the
mouse.

36. I'm not afraid we'll sink because this is a sturdy _____.

37. My father was a _____ businessman in our small city, and it
seemed that everyone knew him.

disclose
his clothes.

38. The caller said his message for my mom was _____, so I got her
from the backyard right away.

bite
plight.

39. The look of _____ on my mother's face indicated that the caller
had given her bad news.

display
dismay.

40. If you ever had the chicken pox, you are _____ to it now and will
not get it again.

41. I wondered where Dad had gone, but he left only a _____ note
that said, "Back soon."

vessel
vessel.

42. House buyers and sellers often have to _____ with each other to
determine the final price.

43. Tina never took lessons, but she seems to have a _____ for golf.

gaudy
body.

44. The inspector needed to _____ whether the car was safe enough
to drive.

45. Passersby responded to our _____ by giving us a push after our
car got stuck in snow.

lack of
knack.

46. The lioness was _____ after four days of unsuccessful hunting,
and so were her cubs.

47. My neighbor wears clothes that are so _____ she looks like she's
dressing up for Halloween.

terse
nurse.

48. If a candidate uses dishonest _____ to try to get elected, you
probably wouldn't want that person to be in office.

49. Mike won't show his birth certificate because it would _____ the
fact that his middle name is Philpot.

"Wait, wait!
Negotiate!"

50. After you pack up the tents, be sure to _____ the campfire.

Lesson 20 _____

anguish *ANG•gwish* NOUN

great pain or suffering of body or mind [We waited in *anguish* to find out if anyone had been saved.]

billow *BIL•oh*

NOUN a great wave [The *billow* that hit our boat nearly sank it.]

VERB **1.** to roll in great waves or clouds [Look at the ocean *billow*.]

VERB **2.** to swell out [The sheets on the clothesline *billow* in the wind.]

dwindle *DWIN•dul* VERB

to keep on becoming smaller or less [Don't allow your savings to *dwindle* away by making unimportant purchases.]

enable *en•AY•bul* VERB

to make able; to provide with strength, power, ability, or opportunity (to do something) [That scholarship will *enable* her to go to college.]

grievance *GREEV•unce* NOUN

something that one is angry or hurt about because of feeling that it is unfair; a complaint about a real or imagined wrong [Any worker here can talk to the boss about any *grievance* he or she has about work.]

grope *GROPE* VERB

1. to feel or search about blindly or uncertainly [I had to *grope* my way down the hall in the dark.]

2. to search for an answer or a solution in an uncertain manner [I didn't know what to say in answer and had to *grope* for the right words to use.]

hence *HENCE* ADVERB

1. therefore; as a result; so [The boxes were large and *hence* awkward to carry.]

2. from this time forward; from now ["Come back six months *hence*," said the dentist.]

hover *HUV•ur* VERB

1. to remain in or near one place in the air [A hummingbird can *hover* by a flower as it feeds.]

2. to remain in one place or stay very close by [Parents often *hover* near their sick child.]

mockery *MOK•ur•ee* NOUN

the act of mocking, or making fun of someone or something [The children's *mockery* of the boy's limp hurt his feelings.]

nonetheless *nun•thuh•LES* ADVERB

in spite of that [The dog wagged its tail, but I was scared of it *nonetheless*.]

pauper *PAW•pur* NOUN

one who is entirely without money; a very poor person [The rich man gave some coins to the *pauper*.]

pell-mell *PEL•MEL* ADVERB

1. in a jumbled or confused way [Don't throw the seeds *pell-mell* into the garden.]

2. in reckless haste [Hearing a scary sound, Byron ran *pell-mell* down the dark street.]

perchance *pur•CHANCE* ADVERB

perhaps [*Perchance* we'll find ourselves on the same team.]

query *KWIHR•ee*

NOUN a request for information; a question [I responded to Jess's *query* by telling him that the rehearsal would be at four o'clock.]

VERB to ask a question or questions [I need to *query* the clerk about the price of this jacket.]

tyrant *TY•runt* NOUN

1. a ruler who has complete control; a cruel ruler [The *tyrant* was fond of throwing people into the dungeon.]

2. anyone who uses power in a cruel or unfair way [Our landlady is a *tyrant* who won't let us hang pictures, paint a wall, or have any kind of pet at all.]

Exercise A: Completion

Choose the correct answer to complete each sentence.

_____ 1. You would have to **grope** for a memory if it was
    A. dim.
    B. sad.
    C. clear

_____ 2. The part of a sailboat that **billows** is the
    A. deck.
    B. mast.
    C. sail.

_____ 3. One thing that causes **anguish** is
    A. a tragedy.
    B. a triumph.
    C. an annoyance.

_____ 4. Someone most people would assume to be a **pauper** is a
    A. jogger.
    B. beggar.
    C. robber.

_____ 5. The punctuation mark that usually goes at the end of a written **query** is
    A. a question mark.
    B. an exclamation point.
    C. a colon.

_____ 6. A person who talks a lot about his or her **grievances** might be called a
    A. bragger.
    B. whiner.
    C. comedian.

Exercise B: Synonyms

Write the **Word** that is a synonym for each set of words.

7. decrease; shrink   _____

8. dictator; slave driver   _____

9. misery; grief   _____

10. hastily; speedily   _____

11. anyway; regardless   _____

12. scorn; disrespect   _____

13. maybe; possibly   _____

14. fumble; seek   _____

15. gripe; injustice   _____

16. assist; support   _____

17. hang; float; flutter   _____

Is it perchance Percy's purpose to propose to pretty Prissy?

Positively!

What'll Dudley do when his dollars all have dwindled down the drain?

"Gotta dime?"

Exercise C: Questions

Write the Word that best answers the question.

18. What will happen to your bank account if you always spend a little more money than you earn?

   _____

19. What might you call a very bossy person who insists on having everything go his or her way?

   _____

20. What would you have to do in order to move around if you were blindfolded?

   _____

21. What is a really bad way to put eggs, bread, and bananas into a grocery bag?

   _____

22. What would a pillowcase do if you held it open in front of a fan?

   _____

23. What can a helicopter do that an airplane cannot do?

   _____

24. What is part of any kind of interview and most kinds of tests?

   _____

25. What is going on when someone is imitated in a cruel way?

   _____

Exercise D: Antonyms

Write the Word that is an antonym for each underlined word or phrase.

26. I wanted Mom to say, "Absolutely! For sure!" but she only said, "___."

   _____

27. Unexpected bad news turned our joy to ___.

   _____

28. I don't intend to go away; I plan to ___ right nearby.

   _____

29. I expected admiration; instead, the reaction was ___.

   _____

30. I cannot get a good, clear answer to my ___.

   _____

31. Do this job slowly and carefully, don't go at it ___!

   _____

32. No, no, no, your appointment was a week ago, not a week ___.

   _____

33. It wasn't because of Sam's pitching that we won; we won ___.

   _____

34. Screens prevent bugs from flying in but ___ fresh air to enter.

   _____

35. The millionaire lost his wealth and became a ___.

   _____

Hansel had to sell all her chickens. Hence Hansel hasn't any hens anymore.

Hugh once floated high over Earth. Now Hugh hovers happily in Heaven.

Exercise E: Fill-in

Write the Word that best completes each sentence. Use each word only once.

36. Jenna had a _____, so she stopped at the Information desk in the lobby.

37. Can you imagine a world without the _____ of war?

38. If you _____ in that drawer, the scissors in it may poke you.

39. My hope that we would win began to _____ as the other team scored run after run.

40. Jeffrey saw a mosquito _____ above his arm and whacked it.

41. When some people have a _____, they go to a lawyer; others try to handle the situation themselves.

42. The king in the story is a _____ who allows his people no freedoms.

43. Racing _____ down the stairs, I missed a step and fell the rest of the way.

44. My cousin Lily often used _____ to poke fun at the way we spoke and behaved, and so we all dreaded her visits.

45. Steam will _____ out when you take the lid off a pot of boiling water.

46. My aunt is so fearful of becoming a _____ that she is extremely careful with her money.

47. A good map will _____ a traveler to find his or her way almost anywhere.

48. It's freezing cold now, but a few months _____, spring will arrive.

49. I asked Wally to leave me alone; _____, he continued to pester me.

50. If I study really hard, _____ I'll get a good grade.

Quick LIST

anguish N.	**enable** V.	**hence** ADV.	**nonetheless** ADV.	**perchance** ADV.
billow N., V.	**grievance** N.	**hover** V.	**pauper** N.	**query** N., V.
dwindle V.	**grope** V.	**mockery** N.	**pell-mell** ADV.	**tyrant** N.

Word Fun 4! _____

Puzzling

Identify the ~~Word~~ from Unit 4 that fits the clue in each box.
The word's first letter is shown in the answer blank.

SIGH_RIGHT_**T**

1. c _____

R I G H T
N O W
! ! ! ! ! ! !

2. u _____

something   chase

3. p _____

Shrink

4. d _____

dan**NOT**ger

5. i _____

fl0at

6. h _____

Crossing

Use the clues in this short, short story to solve the short, short crossword puzzle on the right.

Once upon a time, there was a (1 Across) person who had no money at all. Though poor, he was happy. Until now. Now he faced a (1 Down) serious and difficult problem.

The (2 Across) cruel and very bossy ruler had seen him outside the palace and ordered him to take a bath. Since the poor man didn't own a bathtub or even a bar of soap, he couldn't help but (3 Down) feel angry and annoyed about the order. Then the fellow had a bright idea. Surely the palace had a bathtub and some soap. The guards let him in because he was, after all, just obeying the boss's order!

When the ruler went to brush his teeth, he was a little bit startled, but what could he do?

THE END

Naming

Match each person's name . . .

____ 1. Lee Neeyent

____ 2. Anne Gwish

____ 3. Pa Thet Tikk

____ 4. Dee Lusion

____ 5. Rhea Shurr

____ 6. Ella Kwent

____ 7. E. Senshul

____ 8. Ma Curry

____ 9. Ann Tikk

____ 10. N. Able

to the description it goes best with.

A. She's full of cute tricks.

B. She makes you feel confident.

C. He helps people get things done.

D. Everyone feels really sorry for him.

E. She is a fabulous speaker and writer.

F. He'll let you get away with anything.

G. She won't stop making fun of people.

H. She's always in terrible pain, poor thing!

I. She thinks the sun goes around the Earth!

J. She has a sense of what's truly important.

Digging

Find and underline the Word from Unit 4 that's buried in each sentence. These are the words you need to dig up:

agile	billow	gourmet	morale
ally	gape	mingle	prank

1. Skip ran khaki trousers up the flagpole for a joke.

2. Of course, my jaw dropped and I stared in wonder because I was seeing a peculiar sight!

3. When we play ball, you be on my team, and our side will win.

4. You should try using our method of cooking if you want a truly delicious meal.

5. We need more spirit on our team, or a lesser team will beat us.

6. If "It" tries to catch me when we're playing tag, I leap gracefully out of reach.

7. We joined with them in glee and made one great big, happy group.

8. Bill owes me a ride on his sailboat.

Rhyming

Make each set of lines rhyme (and have a poetic rhythm) by filling in a Word from Unit 4.

1. My rapid feet
   Make me _____.

2. No light at night
   Can be a _____.

3. "How're you, dearie?"
   Was her _____.

4. My poems are worse
   If they're not _____.

Lesson 21 _____

adapt *uh•DAPT* VERB

   1. to make suitable by changing or adjusting [Let's *adapt* this book to make it into a play.]

   2. to adjust (oneself) to a new situation [After growing up on a farm, it took me a while to *adapt* to life in the city.]

boisterous *BOY•stur•us* ADJECTIVE

   noisy and high-spirited   [Children can be *boisterous* when school lets out.]

crave *KRAVE* VERB

   to want very greatly; to long for   [If I go several weeks without pizza, I begin to *crave* it.]

dilemma *dih•LEM•uh* NOUN

   a problem involving a difficult choice [My *dilemma* was that there were bears in the woods and snakes on the riverbank, and I had to go one way or the other.]

haphazard *hap•HAZ•urd* ADJECTIVE

   happening by accident or chance; not done according to a plan   [My brother's *haphazard* grocery shopping resulted in our having twelve boxes of cereal but no milk.]

hesitant *HEZ•uh•tunt* ADJECTIVE

   tending to hesitate; not sure what to do [*Hesitant* about which way to turn, Ed just stood on the corner for several minutes.]

hoax *HOAX* NOUN

   a trick or made-up story that is meant to deceive, especially in fun   [I shortened my brother's favorite pants as a *hoax* to make him think he was getting taller.]

implement *IM•pluh•munt* NOUN

   a tool or instrument   [I need a shovel or other *implement* to move this dirt.]

legible *LEJ•uh•bul* ADJECTIVE

   easy to read; plain and clear   [I know my handwriting is not very *legible*.]

memorable *MEM•ur•uh•bul* ADJECTIVE

   worth remembering; important   [My first sight of the Grand Canyon was a *memorable* moment.]

omit *oh•MIT* VERB

   to leave out   [If you *omit* your address on the form, you won't get a reply.]

Question:

If you have ten dogs and they won't all fit in the car, what must you do?

Answer:
Omit
a mutt
or two.

persist *pur•SIST* VERB

   1. to stick to something; to refuse to give up [A saying that encourages people to *persist* is, "If at first you don't succeed, try, try again."]

   2. to last or stay   [If the heat and dryness *persist*, there will be a water shortage.]

quest *KWEST*

   NOUN   **1.** a seeking, search, or hunt [The hungry boy went on a *quest* for food.]

   NOUN   **2.** a journey in search of adventure [The brave knight set forth on a *quest*.]

   VERB   to seek; to search   [We must *quest* for the truth.]

ramble *RAM•bul* VERB

   1. to walk aimlessly; to wander   [I love to *ramble* through the countryside.]

   2. to talk or write in a wandering manner [Don't *ramble* on and on; get to the point!]

sparse *SPARCE* ADJECTIVE

   thinly scattered; not close together [Trees are *sparse* on Africa's grasslands.]

Exercise A: Synonyms

Write the Word that is closest in meaning
to each set of words and phrases.

1. letting off steam; rough-and-tumble; raising the roof

   _____

2. dragging one's feet; stalling for time; hanging back

   _____

3. give one's right arm for; itch for; ache for; hunger for

   _____

4. nose around; get on the trail of; leave no stone unturned

   _____

5. a practical joke; just make-believe; hocus-pocus

   _____

6. very impressive; staying on one's mind

   _____

7. keep at it; stick to it; never say die

   _____

Exercise C: Antonyms

Write the Word that is an antonym
for each set of words.

17. add; put in

    _____

18. eager; determined

    _____

19. thick; crowded; packed

    _____

20. forgettable; ordinary

    _____

21. careful; deliberate

    _____

22. messy; scrawled

    _____

23. dislike; avoid

    _____

Some people ramble on all fours,
and some ramble on and on.

Exercise B: Yes or No

Circle YES or NO for each question.

8. Do quitters *persist*? . . . .   YES   NO

9. Are all *quests* successful? . . . .   YES   NO

10. Is a tweezers an *implement*? . . . .   YES   NO

11. Do you erase a word to make it *legible*? . . . .   YES   NO

12. Does a person in a hurry tend to *ramble*? . . . .   YES   NO

13. Does being in a *dilemma* make a person happy? . . . .   YES   NO

14. Will your glass hold more to drink if you *omit* the ice? . . . .   YES   NO

15. If you shorten jeans to make them into shorts, do you *adapt* them? . . . .   YES   NO

16. When the fans in the bleachers are *sparse*, can you find a place to sit? . . . .   YES   NO

... so I told her that I ...   ... oh, really, she told me that ...

Exercise D: *If . . .*

Write the Word that best completes each sentence.

24. If I sing at the top of my lungs, jump around, and use the wastebasket for a drum, I am being . . . .

    _____

25. If I have to choose either to jump out a high window or to stay in a burning building, I'm faced with a . . . .

    _____

26. If I can't quite decide whether to go ahead and do something or not, I'm . . . .

    _____

27. If I prefer one of my pens to any other, then I have a favorite writing . . . .

    _____

28. If I scatter a few seeds here and a handful there and a few someplace else, my planting is . . . .

    _____

29. If I take the long way around every chance I get and don't want to be hurried, I like to . . . .

    _____

30. If I bandage my leg and use crutches when there's nothing at all wrong with me, that's a . . . .

    _____

31. If I just can't get used to something new, I'm having trouble learning to . . . .

    _____

Exercise E: *Other Forms of Words*

Add *-y* or *-ly* to Words that are adjectives to make adverbs that answer these questions. (Check a dictionary for the correct way to spell each adverb.)

32. How do the fans of the winning teams at sports events usually behave?

    _____

33. How should warning signs be printed to make sure people understand them?

    _____

34. How do you put things away if you always simply shove them into the closest drawer?

    _____

35. How is Alaska populated? (*Clue:* It's huge but has very few people.)

    _____

Question:
What do you call it when some joker with a fake flower squirts water in people's faces?

Answer: A hoax that soaks folks

Quick LIST
adapt V.
boisterous ADJ.
crave V.
dilemma N.
haphazard ADJ.
hesitant ADJ.
hoax N.
implement N.
legible ADJ.
memorable ADJ.
omit V.
persist V.
quest N., V.
ramble V.
sparse ADJ.

Exercise F: Fill-in

Write the Word that best completes each sentence. Use each word only once.

36. The hair on my grandpa's head is _____ and will soon be gone.

37. It's all right to be _____ at a party, as long as your activities don't disturb the neighbors.

38. If your cough and fever _____ for more than a couple of days, you should see a doctor.

39. A poem I read a year ago was so _____ that I can still quote lines from it.

40. A spoon is a better _____ than a fork for eating cereal.

41. The words carved on the stone were no longer _____ because they had been rubbed almost smooth.

42. Let's carry some sandwiches and just _____ through the woods until we get hungry.

43. I was in a _____ when I had to decide whether to hurt my friend's feelings or to tell a lie.

44. Our dog sheds every spring to _____ to the hot weather that's coming.

45. Pillows arranged under my blanket worked as a _____ to make my sister think I was in bed and sound asleep.

46. Hundreds of books were stacked in a _____ way all over the library tables.

47. Some mornings I am so tired that I _____ just a few more minutes of sleep.

48. Many an early explorer went on a _____ for gold in the Southwest, but most did not find it.

49. If you want to learn, you can't be _____ about asking questions when you don't understand something.

50. I'm so angry with Ken that I plan to _____ any mention of him from my thank-you speech.

Adapting to
a new place

Adapting to
getting older

Adapting to
technology

Adapting to
new rules

Adapting to
being omitted

Lesson 22 _____

extract ek•STRAKT VERB

1. to pull out; to draw out [I hope the dentist doesn't need to *extract* my tooth.]

2. to get out by pressing or squeezing [Wring the towel to *extract* water from it.]

frail *FRAIL* ADJECTIVE

1. slender and delicate; weak [My uncle's illness has left him so *frail* that he can't walk.]

2. easily broken or damaged [That old chair is too *frail* to support my weight.]

gawk *GAWK* VERB

to stare rudely or stupidly because of curiosity or amazement [I didn't want everyone to know I was a tourist, so I tried not to *gawk* at the unusual clothes and buildings.]

ingenious in•JEEN•yus ADJECTIVE

1. very clever and inventive [George Washington was an *ingenious* military leader.]

2. cleverly planned and made [This *ingenious* tool can get the top off any jar.]

insistent in•SIS•tunt ADJECTIVE

demanding strongly and, usually, repeatedly [My brother was *insistent* about wanting to go, so we took him with us.]

interrogate in•TAIR•uh•gate VERB

to ask questions of; to examine or get information from by asking questions [The lawyer will *interrogate* the witness.]

irreplaceable ih•rih•PLAY•suh•bul

ADJECTIVE that cannot be replaced [An original painting is *irreplaceable*.]

lair *LAIR* NOUN

the bed or resting place of a wild animal [The fox returned to its *lair* every night.]

luminous LOO•muh•nus ADJECTIVE

giving off light; shining [The stars are *luminous*.]

morsel MOR•sul NOUN

1. a small bite or bit of food [He barely ate a *morsel*.]

2. any small amount or piece [I haven't a *morsel* of energy left.]

neutral NOO•trul ADJECTIVE

not joining either side in a disagreement or war [Many countries remained *neutral* in the war.]

sullen SUL•un ADJECTIVE

silent and unfriendly because one feels angry, bitter, or hurt [When Ethan doesn't get what he wants, he becomes *sullen*.]

sultry SUL•tree ADJECTIVE

very hot and damp, without a breeze [On a *sultry* day, the beach is very crowded.]

surge *SURJ*

NOUN 1. a large wave of water or its violent rushing motion [The *surge* knocked us over.]

NOUN 2. any sudden, strong rush [The *surge* of the crowd nearly crushed us.]

VERB to move in a surge [The fans at the stadium *surged* around us.]

vengeance VEN•junce NOUN

the act of getting even for a wrong; punishment in return for harm done [When I insulted Ron, he took *vengeance* by embarrassing me.]

THE PATH IN THE WOODS PART 1

A girl walks sullenly down a path. It's a sultry evening, and she is hot, lost, tired, and hungry. (*"Is that tasty-looking morsel a mushroom or a rock? Yuck! A toad! Ohhh."*) She goes on.

Exercise A: Rhyme Time
Write the **Word** that completes each rhyme.

1. That fellow is so thin and pale
   I fear he must be rather . . . . _____

2. A statue that began to talk
   Would surely make me stop and . . . . _____

3. I yanked and tugged and pulled, but it's a fact,
   A nail can be a hard thing to . . . . _____

4. I hope the ink you drew with is the kind that is erasable.
   The tablecloth you made the picture on is . . . . _____

The girl stops suddenly when a strange voice interrogates her. ("Whooo? Whoo? Whoo are yoo?") An owl blinks at her from its branch in a tree, and the girl rushes on. ("I'm not scared of yooooo!")

Exercise B: Other Forms of Words
Use what you know about the **Words** to choose the correct answers.

_____ 5. What is a person with **ingenuity** very good at?
   A. sympathizing   B. obeying orders   C. solving problems

_____ 6. Which of the following is an **interrogative** sentence?
   A. "I can!"   B. "Why try?"   C. "They went."

_____ 7. During a baseball game, whose behavior must show **neutrality**?
   A. a coach's   B. a player's   C. an umpire's

_____ 8. What is used for **extractions**?
   A. a thumbtack   B. a tweezers   C. a scissors

_____ 9. What part of an oak tree has the most **frailty**?
   A. a twig   B. an acorn   C. the trunk

_____ 10. What does a person usually do **sullenly**?
   A. yell   B. pout   C. yawn

Exercise C: Antonyms
Write the **Word** that is an antonym for each of these words. This exercise continues on the next page.

11. cool _____

12. peek _____

13. insert _____

14. trickle _____

At the path's end, she gawks at a tiny house and its mailbox. ("Bears' Lair. Cutesy.") Feeling surges of hunger, she insistently knocks, then goes inside, uninvited.

15. stupid _____

16. answer _____

17. cheerful _____

18. forgiveness _____

Now frail from hunger, the girl extracts all the food from the cupboards—every can, bag, box, and bottle of . . . porridge! *("Ma Bear must be an ingenious cook!")* She eats it all—too hot, too cold, and some that's sort of neutral.

Exercise D: Questions
Write the Word that best answers the question.

19. What is a judge supposed to be? _____

20. What is weather like in a jungle? _____

21. What might knock you off your feet? _____

22. Where does a wild bear spend the winter? _____

23. What describes a quilt your great-grandmother made? _____

24. What do the police do to someone suspected of a crime? _____

25. What describes a person who just won't take no for an answer? _____

26. What do a car's headlights become when they're turned on? _____

27. What might you do if you could hardly believe your eyes? _____

28. What is a chocolate chip? _____

("This porridge stuff doesn't have a lot of flavor, but it does stick to the ribs!")

Quick LIST
extract V.
frail ADJ.
gawk V.
ingenious ADJ.
insistent ADJ.
interrogate V.
irreplaceable ADJ.
lair N.
luminous ADJ.
morsel N.
neutral ADJ.
sullen ADJ.
sultry ADJ.
surge N., V.
vengeance N.

Exercise E: Synonyms
Write the Word that is a synonym for each set of words.

29. den; burrow; resting place _____

30. glum; moody; grumpy _____

31. sliver; tidbit; fragment _____

32. revenge; getting even _____

33. creative; original _____

34. bright; glowing _____

35. fragile; feeble _____

Exercise F: Fill-in

Write the **Word** that best completes each sentence. Use each word only once.

36. The most uncomfortable days of summer are the really _____ ones.

37. The forest rangers tracked the bobcat back to its _____.

38. The boards had rotted, making the porch too _____ to be safe.

39. My dog Rex is one of a kind; he is truly _____.

40. I apologized to my brother, but his _____ silence told me I wasn't forgiven.

41. Germany invaded several _____ countries that hadn't taken sides in the war.

42. A person who wants _____ looks for a way to "get even."

43. My sister was so _____ about playing another game that I gave in.

44. Dad began to _____ me about where I'd been and what I'd done.

45. Will you help me _____ this splinter in my foot?

46. We watched the waves _____ toward the shore.

47. Many people are grateful to the _____ woman who invented the dishwasher.

48. We were so hungry that we ate every _____, and not a crumb was left.

49. I can read my watch in the dark, thanks to its _____ face.

50. Someone who'd never seen a giraffe would probably _____ at the sight of one.

Moving through the now-dark house, the girl bumps into something and hears glass crash to the floor. *("I hope that wasn't irreplaceable.")* She steps on something else, and a TV comes on. *("Aha! It's a remote control!")* Settling into a big chair, she skips through the channels. *("What? No cable?")*

A familiar luminous glow catches her eye. Wandering into a small bedroom, she finds the computer and sits down. *("Maybe I can go online!")*

TO BE CONTINUED

Exercise G: Writing

Now that you've read Part 1 of "The Path in the Woods," what do you think happens in Part 2? On your own paper, write *your* ideas about what happens next. If you like, you can write a whole ending of your own. Use at least THREE **Words**.

Lesson 23

accusation *ak•yoo•ZAY•shun* NOUN
a claim that someone has done something wrong [Just because someone makes an *accusation* doesn't mean that it's true.]

alter *ALL•tur* VERB
to make something different without changing it into something else [A tailor can *alter* clothing so that it fits better.]

benefactor *ben•uh•FAK•tur* NOUN
one who does good to another; one who gives a gift [An unnamed *benefactor* donated many boxes of books to our library.]

dilapidated *dih•LAP•uh•day•tid* ADJECTIVE
falling apart, especially from being neglected [The shed was so *dilapidated*, it looked ready to fall down.]

fickle *FIK•ul* ADJECTIVE
tending to change frequently; not dependable [My *fickle* cat often turns up her nose at food she loved just the day before.]

negligence *NEG•lih•jence* NOUN
the failure to give the proper attention or care to something [The poor condition of the park is the result of the city's *negligence*.]

---

optimist *OP•tuh•mist* NOUN
a person who looks on the bright side and tends to think that everything will turn out for the best [My sister the *optimist* sees one snowflake and starts thinking about sledding and snowballs.]

pessimist *PES•uh•mist* NOUN
a person who sees the worst in every situation and tends to think that everything will turn out badly [My brother the *pessimist* sees a snowflake and starts worrying about getting cold and wet.]

---

rational *RASH•un•ul* ADJECTIVE
able to think in a careful way without being controlled by emotion; acting in a reasonable way [People who lose their tempers are not *rational*.]

savor *SAY•vur* VERB
to enjoy to the fullest [I *savor* every moment I'm horseback riding.]

smug *SMUG* ADJECTIVE
too pleased or satisfied with oneself [Sally never seems surprised by praise; she always looks *smug*.]

Sally was smug, but Timmy waited for *his* grade with more tentative feelings.

tentative *TEN•tuh•tiv* ADJECTIVE
uncertain; not definite or final [We made *tentative* plans for a picnic, but everything depends on the weather.]

unaccountable *un•uh•KOWN•tuh•bul* ADJECTIVE not possible to explain; strange [We saw an *unaccountable* light in the sky and wondered if it was a UFO.]

urban *UR•bun* ADJECTIVE
having to do with the city [*Urban* areas offer museums, shows, and great restaurants as well as crowding, traffic jams, and dirty air.]

verify *VAIR•uh•fy* VERB
to prove the truth of [Do you have a doctor's note to *verify* that you were absent due to illness?]

Exercise A: Yes or No

Circle YES or NO for each question.

1. On the day of a track meet,
   are the plans for the meet usually **tentative**? . . . . YES NO

2. Would you **savor** a really delicious dinner? . . . . YES NO

3. Does a **pessimist** feel enthusiastic and eager? . . . . . . YES NO

4. Do people use I.D. cards to **verify** who they are? . . . . YES NO

5. Is it **negligence** to feed, walk, and play with a dog? . . . YES NO

6. Is it difficult to **alter** something written in pencil? . . . . YES NO

7. Can you expect to hear **accusations** in court? . . . . . . YES NO

8. Do you expect to find cows in an **urban** area? . . . . . . YES NO

9. Is it a good idea to count on a **fickle** friend? . . . . YES NO

Nigel could do some amazing tricks, but a moment of negligence during takeoff . . .

. . . brought an unexpected landing.

Exercise B: If . . .

Write the **Word** that best completes each sentence. This exercise continues on the next page.

10. If I'm often proud of myself and think that most people wish they were as special as I am, I'm . . . . _____

11. If you say I took your book but then you find it in your locker, you'd probably regret your . . . . _____

12. If I like someone best on Monday but someone else on Thursday and have a new best friend the next week, I'm . . . . _____

13. If I'm gloomy and hopeless and usually assume I'll lose or fail or make mistakes or be blamed for things, I'm a . . . . _____

14. If someone buys a washing machine and dryer for a homeless shelter, that person is a . . . . _____

15. If something is mysterious, and you can't imagine what made it happen, it's . . . . _____

16. If I think I might be able to go to the movies but I'm not sure, my plans to meet you there are . . . . _____

17. If I believe that life is an adventure and tomorrow's going to be even better than today, I'm a real . . . . _____

18. If you think things through and are ruled by your head, not your heart, you're a ___ person. . . . . _____

19. If I say it's raining and you doubt me, I could open the curtains and point outdoors to ___ it. . . . . _____

Exercise C: Nicknames

Write the Word that describes or names the person who would have each nickname.

20. Charitable Charlie

_____

21. Hopeful Hannah

_____

22. Gloomy Gilbert

_____

23. Downtown Danny

_____

Exercise D: Synonyms

Write the Word that is a synonym for each set of words.

24. appreciate; like _____

25. change; adjust _____

26. donor; giver _____

27. carelessness; neglect _____

28. sensible; wise _____

29. run-down; broken-down _____

Exercise E: Antonyms

Write the Word that is an antonym for each set of words.

30. constant; unchanging _____

31. firm; sure _____

32. undamaged; well-kept _____

33. insecure; humble _____

34. rural; country _____

35. ordinary; understandable _____

Quick LIST

accusation N.	**negligence** N.	**smug** ADJ.
alter V.	**optimist** N.	**tentative** ADJ.
benefactor N.	**pessimist** N.	**unaccountable** ADJ.
dilapidated ADJ.	**rational** ADJ.	**urban** ADJ.
fickle ADJ.	**savor** V.	**verify** V.

Exercise F: Fill-In

Write the Word that best completes each sentence. Use each word only once.

36. The drama club members need a _____ to buy them new lights.

37. There are many apartment buildings in my _____ neighborhood.

38. The result of my _____ is that I have a garden filled with weeds and dead flowers.

39. We decided to _____ our plans and go bowling instead of to a movie.

40. An _____ who is late for the bus believes there's a good chance the bus will also be late.

41. The doctor measured me to _____ how much I'd grown in the past year.

42. It's difficult to remain _____ when you're in love, really excited, or mad as a wet hen.

43. My answer has to be _____ because I'm just not sure yet about the situation.

44. Jody's so _____ about her talent that she figures no one else has a chance in the contest.

45. I am angry about your _____ that I cheated, and I'm sure you can't prove it.

46. Greg is such a _____ that whenever the phone rings, he thinks it's bad news.

47. My notebook is so _____ that the pages are falling out and the cover's almost gone.

48. For some _____ reason, my cat sometimes leaps suddenly in the air.

49. Let's not go in for dinner yet; let's _____ the sunset for a while.

50. My brother had a _____ girlfriend . . . but not for very long!

Since Opal had never bowled before, her optimism was quite unaccountable. On the other hand, Pepe was pessimistic about his new teammate and couldn't bear even to watch or listen. Later, Opal, Pepe, and the whole team savored their victory.

Lesson 24

bliss *BLIS* NOUN

great happiness; perfect joy [I awoke on the first day of vacation with a sense of *bliss*.]

confidential *kon•fuh•DEN•shul* ADJECTIVE

spoken or written as a secret [What I'm telling you is *confidential*, so keep it between us.]

drawback *DRAW•bak* NOUN

a disadvantage; anything that makes something less satisfactory [A *drawback* to a Tuesday night party is that no one can stay up late.]

elegant *EL•uh•gunt* ADJECTIVE

beautiful in a simple and graceful way; classy [The *elegant* dress revealed Nicole's talents as a designer.]

extinguish *ek•STING•gwish* VERB

to put out, as a fire; to put an end to [If it rains, that will *extinguish* both the fire and my hopes for a warm night.]

finicky *FIN•uh•kee* ADJECTIVE

very choosy; picky [My cousins are *finicky* about what they will eat.]

haggle *HAG•ul* VERB

to argue over price [Some people hate shopping for a car because it is common to have to *haggle* over the price.]

jeer *JEER* VERB

to make sounds or speak in a way that makes fun of someone or something [Did you hear the crowd *jeer* when I missed my sixth free throw in a row?]

lament *luh•MENT*

NOUN an expression of deep sorrow [I heard the child's *lament* when she realized that her mother had left.]

VERB to express deep sorrow; to mourn; to regret [When she retires, we will *lament* the loss of Ms. Riddle, who is the best teacher in the school.]

notorious *no•TOR•ee•us* ADJECTIVE

famous for something bad [Mr. Hicks groaned when he saw that the most *notorious* student in school would be in his class.]

peril *PAIR•ul* NOUN

danger [The climber was in great *peril* as she inched her way along the ledge.]

ploy *PLOY* NOUN

a trick that is meant to get the better of someone or to fool someone into doing something [His promise to help me later was just a *ploy* to get my help when he needed it.]

rash *RASH* ADJECTIVE

hasty and not thought out [She made a *rash* statement that she was soon sorry for.]

strenuous *STREN•yoo•us* ADJECTIVE

requiring much energy and strength [After Gina's operation, the doctor told her not to take part in *strenuous* activity.]

whim *WIM* NOUN

a sudden wish that is not based in need or deep feeling [I bought the purple baseball cap on a *whim*.]

CHEERS
Some people say bungee-jumping is a sport that brings bliss.

JEERS
Others say it is not a sport at all and that it puts people in peril.

Exercise A: *If...*

Write the Word that best completes each sentence.

1. If you shop and shop for the perfect shirt, eat only a certain cereal, and wear only one kind of socks, you are .... _____

2. If you're on a mountaintop and the snow is so deep you can't see the trail and your two-way radio just broke, you are in .... _____

3. If your parents set the table with a white tablecloth, the best dishes, and a vase of flowers, they probably want the table to look .... _____

4. If you are exhausted and sweaty when a job is done, and your muscles ache and you have blisters, the work was .... _____

5. If you're at the mall and see something you're not shopping for but like it and buy it on the spot, your purchase is the result of a ...... _____

6. If a company offers you a free gift but you have to pay ▯5.00 for "mailing costs," that offer of a "free" gift was a .... _____

7. If you love going to garage sales and trying to talk the seller into reducing a fifty-cent price to a quarter, you like to .... _____

8. If your dad just told you what he got your mom for her birthday and he can't wait to surprise her, what he told you was .... _____

9. If you quit the team because you got mad and then you spend the rest of the season regretting it, your decision was .... _____

10. If you feel like you're walking on air, and life is wonderful, and there's a smile on your face and another in your heart, you feel ... _____

Exercise B: *True or False*

Circle TRUE or FALSE for each statement.

11. Any sale is a ***ploy*** to get people into a store to shop. .... TRUE   FALSE

12. A baseball cap would be an ***elegant*** addition to any outfit. .... TRUE   FALSE

13. It is important to ***extinguish*** any fire you make in the forest. .... TRUE   FALSE

14. Some people are ***notorious*** for being kind and doing good works. .... TRUE   FALSE

15. Most people are pleased and flattered if others ***jeer*** at them. .... TRUE   FALSE

16. Getting healthy exercise is a ***drawback*** to sports activities. .... TRUE   FALSE

17. A fancy restaurant is a good place to ***haggle*** over a price. .... TRUE   FALSE

18. Mowing a hill with a push mower is ***strenuous*** work. .... TRUE   FALSE

Exercise C: Synonyms

Write the Word that is a synonym for each of these words.

19. private   _____

20. bargain   _____

21. reckless   _____

22. smother   _____

23. fussy   _____

24. grieve   _____

Exercise D: Analogies

Write the letter of the word pair that completes the analogy.

____ 25. *extinguish* : *flame* ::
      A. run : walk   C. grow : plant
      B. fly : bird   D. erase : drawing

____ 26. *contentment* : *bliss* ::
      A. fear : terror   C. sadness : gladness
      B. faith : belief   D. thirst : hunger

____ 27. *jeer* : *scorn* ::
      A. drink : liquid   C. bandage : wound
      B. recall : past   D. scold : criticism

____ 28. *selective* : *finicky* ::
      A. tall : heavy   C. large : gigantic
      B. plain : pretty   D. delicious : sweet

LAMENTS

Diver: "My lament is that the ocean has become so polluted."

Fish: "My lament is that the ocean has become so polluted . . . with people."

Exercise E: Rhyme Time

Write the Word that completes each rhyme.

29. I thought the crowd would clap and cheer.
    I blushed when all they did was ___.

    _____

30. Your heart is made of pure cement
    If it's not touched by my ___.

    _____

31. Don't give a fool a lot of cash,
    Or he just might do something ___.

    _____

32. A wolf reached for a porcupine,
        but then he yanked his paw back.
    He'd planned on having dinner,
        but the quills were quite a ___.

    _____

33. I hadn't planned to take a swim
    But jumped in on a sudden ___.

    _____

34. Be careful if you go to Gloria's
    For her dog is quite ___.

    _____

35. Careful Carl and cautious Carol
    Always stay away from ___.

    _____

Exercise F: Writing

On your own paper, write a paragraph describing something that you believe could put you in **peril**. Use at least TWO Words in your description.

Exercise G: Fill-in

Write the **Word** that best completes each sentence. Use each word only once.

CHEERS and **JEERS**

The pass was high and smooth and elegant.

I caught it like I would an elephant.

36. Losing your temper may make you do _____ things.

37. It is just plain mean to _____ at those who are trying their best to succeed at something.

38. People often make a wish before they _____ the candles on a birthday cake.

39. I _____ the loss of the locket Grandma gave me.

40. Is wanting a really short haircut just a _____, or have you given it much thought?

41. Jesse James was a _____ bank robber.

42. The moving van was part of a _____ to make the neighbors believe that the burglars were actually movers.

43. There wasn't any real _____ from the storm, even though it was noisy and scary.

44. I refuse to _____ over my babysitting rates.

45. Satin curtains make the room look _____ in the evening light.

46. For me, a _____ to living in southern California is that I don't get to see much snow.

47. Is what you've told me _____, or may I tell Brad?

48. I'm _____ about what I put on the walls because how my room looks is important to me.

TEARS and **JEERS**

Hiking through poison oak could be a rash activity.

49. Carl was filled with _____ as he looked forward to a whole day of nothing but fun and relaxation at the beach.

50. Jack's construction job is _____, but he enjoys it.

Quick LIST

bliss N.	**finicky** ADJ.	**peril** N.
confidential ADJ.	**haggle** V.	**ploy** N.
drawback N.	**jeer** V.	**rash** ADJ.
elegant ADJ.	**lament** N., V.	**strenuous** ADJ.
extinguish V.	**notorious** ADJ.	**whim** N.

Lesson 25

administer ad•MIN•us•tur VERB

    1. to manage; to direct the affairs of [Who will *administer* the baseball league at the park?]

    2. to carry out; to give; to supply [Emergency rooms can *administer* medical help quickly.]

barbaric bar•BAIR•ik ADJECTIVE

    uncivilized; crude and cruel [Whipping someone as a punishment seems very *barbaric* to me.]

chipper CHIP•ur ADJECTIVE

    cheerful and energetic [You look *chipper*!]

cluster KLUS•tur

    NOUN a number of things growing, collected, or lying together [A *cluster* of tulips grew beside the front door.]

    VERB to grow or gather in a cluster [Children often *cluster* in the park after school.]

consecutive kun•SEK•yoo•tiv ADJECTIVE

    following in regular order without a break [The temperature was below zero for eight *consecutive* days.]

culprit KUL•prit NOUN

    one guilty of a crime or wrongdoing [The *culprit* was captured after a police chase.]

dispute dis•PYOOT

    NOUN an argument; a debate [There was a *dispute* over the umpire's call.]

    VERB to question or deny the truth or rightness of [Do you *dispute* my statement?]

ember EM•bur NOUN

    a glowing piece of coal or wood in the ashes from a fire [A single *ember* can start a huge forest fire.]

jest JEST

    NOUN a joke, amusing remark, or playful act [He made a *jest* about my appearance.]

    VERB to say something funny; to joke [People are more likely to *jest* when they're in a good mood.]

materialize muh•TEER•ee•ul•ize VERB

    1. to become actual or real [I fear my dream won't *materialize*.]

    2. to give something a physical form or to take on a physical form [With her knitting needles, my aunt rapidly made a scarf *materialize* from a ball of yarn.]

omen OH•mun NOUN

    anything that is supposed to be a sign of a future event, whether good or bad [Are you one of the people who think that breaking a mirror is a bad *omen*?]

spendthrift SPEND•thrift

    NOUN a person who spends his or her money carelessly [The *spendthrift* went bankrupt.]

    ADJECTIVE wasteful with one's money [She'll regret her *spendthrift* ways.]

tier TEER NOUN

    one of a series of layers or rows, arranged one above another [We sat in the second *tier* of seats.]

vegetation veh•juh•TAY•shun NOUN

    things growing from the soil; plant life [The yard is covered in thick *vegetation*.]

writhe RITHE VERB

    to twist and turn; to twist about [Watching the dancers *writhe*, I thought they looked as if they were in great pain.]

THE PATH IN THE WOODS PART 2

Three travelers follow the path. One speaks in a chipper voice. (*"Why is it night? Are we almost home? There's a toad! Are toads vegetation?"*) A tired voice replies. (*"No, Teddy."*)

Exercise A: Synonyms

Write the Word that is a synonym for each set of words.

1. bunch; clump

2. happy; lively; carefree

3. wild; savage

4. develop; appear

5. criminal; outlaw

6. indication; warning; hint

7. squirm; bend

8. in a row; continuous

9. shrubs; greenery

10. lead; govern

Exercise B: What Is It?

Write the Word that each clue describes.

11. It helps you see well if you sit in it.
    A number of seats often fit in it.

12. It has no flames, but it is hot.
    Though not a lamp, it gleams a lot.

13. It can, or so some people think, forecast
    The future, but it cannot tell the past.

14. A group of people stand in this to chatter.
    But it is gone the instant that they scatter.

15. It may make people groan, or they may love it.
    But no one wants to be the victim of it.

16. It's there when one side thinks the other's wrong.
    It isn't there when people get along.

17. Farmers work to grow it, but they also pull it out.
    Some of it they want, but some they'd rather do without.

Home at last, the travelers find their front door wide open.

Papa says, "Is this a jest?"

Mama says, "Is this an omen?"

Teddy says, "Is this a spendthrift? That's a vocabulary word I learned this week."

After a look around the living room, Papa speaks, his eyes glowing like embers. "Some nasty culprit has moved my recliner and used up the batteries in the remote control!"

Almost in tears, Mama speaks. "Some barbaric creature has eaten all our porridge and left a whole cluster of my crystal kiddy people broken on the floor!"

Exercise C: Yes or No

Circle YES or NO for each question.

18. Are these numbers in **consecutive** order: 2, 4, 8, 6? . . . .   YES   NO

19. Is an **ember** something people hold in their hands? . . . .   YES   NO

20. Does a **spendthrift** save lots of money in the bank? . . . .   YES   NO

21. Are the seats in a movie theater arranged in **tiers**? . . . .   YES   NO

22. Does a mayor **administer** the affairs of a city? . . . .   YES   NO

23. Are corn and wheat examples of **vegetation**? . . . .   YES   NO

24. Does a **culprit** deserve blame? . . . .   YES   NO

25. Do grapes grow in a **cluster**? . . . .   YES   NO

Exercise D: Antonyms

Write the Word that is an antonym for each set of words.

26. agree; support   _____

27. miser; tightwad   _____

28. weary; gloomy; dull   _____

29. gentle; kind; civilized   _____

30. disappear; fade; crumble   _____

Exercise E: Questions

Write the Word that best answers the question.

31. What does a police officer try to find?   _____

32. What do you do when you clown around or crack a joke?   _____

33. What would a superstitious person pay great attention to?   _____

34. What do dogs do when they scratch their backs on the ground?   _____

35. What are you if your allowance is always gone the same day you get it?   _____

In his turn, Teddy speaks. "Why do we talk in consecutive order most of the time, and who has been using my computer, and who ordered all that expensive stuff on the Internet, and who charged it all on Papa's credit card? *And, most of all, who is SHE?*"

_____

Quick LIST

administer V.
barbaric ADJ.
chipper ADJ.
cluster N., V.
consecutive ADJ.
culprit N.
dispute N., V.
ember N.
jest N., V.
materialize V.
omen N.
spendthrift N., ADJ.
tier N.
vegetation N.
writhe V.

Exercise F: Fill-in

Write the **Word** that best completes each sentence. Use each word only once.

36. His _____ made everyone roar with laughter.

37. On the top _____ of the wedding cake, there was a little statue of a bride and groom.

38. There is so much _____ in her back yard that it looks like a jungle.

39. My sister is such a _____ that she is always running out of cash.

40. Greg greeted me with a _____ "Good morning!" that made it clear he was feeling great.

41. I am really tired of this _____; can we just agree to disagree?

42. Okay, who is the _____ who broke Mr. Cobb's window? Confess!

43. A group of _____ invaders drove the people from their homes and burned the city.

44. You shouldn't _____ all the little statues together; spread them out so everyone can see them.

45. After it had rained for six _____ days, we all had to deal with flooded basements.

46. A red sunset is supposed to be an _____ that the next day's weather will be fine.

47. Our plans for a vacation trip did not _____ because Mom couldn't take time off from work.

48. You help those people over there, and I'll _____ aid to the ones on this side.

49. We didn't leave our campsite until every last _____ had been put out.

50. The girl had awful stomach cramps that made her _____ in pain.

The girl materializes from who-knows-where. "Oh!" She smiles. "Hi! I bet you folks are the Bears, huh? I was on my way to Grandma's and got lost and saw your nice little house and so I , uh, . . . Would anyone like some of my, uh, your popcorn?"

"You guys eat only vegetation-type food, right?"

THE END

Word Fun 5!

Puzzling

Identify the Word from Unit 5 that fits the clue in each box.
The word's first letter is shown in the answer blank.

1. w _____

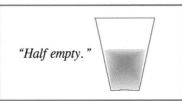

"Half empty."

2. p _____

"Half full!"

3. o _____

4. b _____

f   e   w

5. s _____

thing
thing thing thing
thing   thing
thing

6. c _____

7. l _____

Naming

Match each person's name . . .

____ 1. Bennie Fakter

____ 2. X. Tingwish

____ 3. Barb Erick

____ 4. Chip Purr

____ 5. Ella Gunt

Matching

Match the phrases . . .

____ 1. omit a bit

____ 2. a rash dash

____ 3. a hare's lair

____ 4. crave a cave

____ 5. appear to jeer

____ 6. suggest a quest

____ 7. savor the flavor

____ 8. my folks' hoax

____ 9. a fruit dispute

____ 10. the best jest

____ 11. verify a buy

____ 12. a frail male

Defining

Match the invented word . . .

____ 1. delima

____ 2. boysterous

____ 3. vegenation

____ 4. confidental

____ 5. accluesation

to the description it goes best with.

A. He's lively and cheerful.

B. She's always beautifully dressed.

C. He gives his money to the needy.

D. She always blows out the candles.

E. She's cruel and not very civilized.

that are closest in meaning.

A. seem to sneer

B. the greatest gag

C. leave out a little

D. prove a purchase

E. deeply desire a den

F. a rabbit's resting place

G. a battle over bananas

H. my parents' prank

I. propose a pursuit

J. treasure the taste

K. a breakable boy

L. a reckless race

with its meaning.

A. a country's flowers and trees

B. a problem involving vegetables

C. what male children are when they're making noise

D. a criticism you make that is based on a piece of evidence

E. what your secrets are if you tell them while getting a filling

A-maze-ing

As a maze, this puzzle is not too amazing, but you do have to know the words from Unit 5—and your directions. (And it will help to know some words both backwards and forwards!)

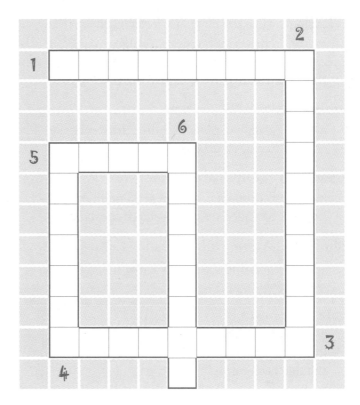

1 RIGHT	easy to keep in mind; hard to forget
2 DOWN	what Smokey the Bear wants you to do to your campfire
3 LEFT *	every which way; not carefully done
4 UP **	what you face when you're "between a rock and a hard place"
5 RIGHT	to change or modify, as a tailor does to tight pants
6 DOWN	sensible, reasonable, practical; not crazy

* Here, "left" means backwards from right to left.

** Here, "up" means backwards from bottom to top.

Lesson 26

alien *AY•lee•un*

ADJECTIVE **1.** belonging to another country or people; foreign [Foods that were once *alien* to Americans are now commonly served.]

ADJECTIVE **2.** entirely different from one's own; strange [It can be hard to adjust to *alien* customs while traveling in a foreign country.]

NOUN a person who is not a citizen of the country in which he or she lives; a foreigner [Many *aliens* live in the United States.]

aroma *uh•ROH•muh* NOUN

a smell, usually a pleasant one; a fragrance [A pine tree has a delightful *aroma*.]

boundless *BOWND•lus* ADJECTIVE

having no borders or boundaries; unlimited [A good education makes job choices *boundless*.]

din *DIN* NOUN

a continuing loud noise [The *din* in the factory was deafening.]

gale *GALE* NOUN

1. a strong wind [The *gale* made us stumble backwards.]

2. an outburst, as of laughter [My joke was met with a *gale* of laughter.]

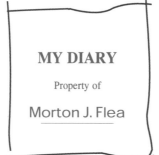

MY DIARY

Property of

Morton J. Flea

hamper *HAM•pur* VERB

to keep from moving or acting freely; to get in the way of [Snow can *hamper* a mail carrier's ability to make deliveries.]

intercept *in•tur•SEPT* VERB

to take, seize, or stop on the way; to cut off [Did enemy soldiers *intercept* our messenger?]

liable *LY•uh•bul* ADJECTIVE

1. bound by law or what is right; responsible [Since it was our fault, we are *liable*.]

2. likely to do or cause something [If you keep spinning, you're *liable* to make yourself dizzy.]

maneuver *muh•NOO•vur*

NOUN **1.** a carefully planned move, as of troops in battle [George Washington's clever *maneuver* surprised the British troops.]

NOUN **2.** any skillful change of movement or direction [Mom made a quick *maneuver* to avoid the car that was heading toward us.]

VERB to move or to carry out a maneuver [It can be tiring to *maneuver* a loaded shopping cart around.]

minute *my•NOOT* ADJECTIVE

1. tiny; very small [There was a *minute* speck of dust on the table.]

2. going into small details; exact [I gave Sandy *minute* directions to my house.]

proposition *prop•uh•ZIH•shun* NOUN

something proposed; a plan [Let's take a vote on Jeffrey's *proposition*.]

scowl *SKOWL*

VERB to look angry or mean by lowering the eyebrows and frowning [The angry old woman *scowled* at us.]

NOUN an angry look [The man's *scowl* revealed his anger.]

spontaneous *spon•TAY•nee•us* ADJECTIVE

1. done in a free and natural way, without much thought or planning [We broke into *spontaneous* cheers when we heard the news.]

2. occurring naturally, without an outside cause or force [No one can control a volcano's eruption; it is entirely *spontaneous*.]

submerge *sub•MURJ* VERB

to put or go into water; to stay underwater [A submarine is designed to *submerge*.]

wiry *WY•ree* ADJECTIVE

1. of or like wire; stiff [I can't make my *wiry* hair lie flat.]

2. thin and strong [I'm not big and muscular, but I'm *wiry*.]

Exercise A: Synonyms

Write the Word that is a synonym for each of these words.

1. suggestion   _____

2. dunk   _____

3. gust   _____

4. scent   _____

5. racket   _____

Exercise B: Antonyms

Write the Word that is an antonym for each of these words.

6. huge   _____

7. grin   _____

8. limited   _____

9. assist   _____

10. native   _____

11. husky   _____

12. planned   _____

MONDAY
Big gale today hampered my activity. Settled in some little kid's wiry hair. Not so comfy, but feels safe. Nice kid, I guess. For a human being.

TUESDAY
Peeked out this A.M. and saw giant alien scowl.

Leaped off the kid's head just in time to escape getting totally submerged in hot, soapy water! ACK!!

That stuff's likely to kill some poor flea someday! Dumb humans! Well, time for this poor flea to flee!

Exercise C: Questions

Write the Word that best answers the question.

13. What are whales able to do for a long time between breaths?   _____

14. What would someone from the United States be while he or she was living in Ireland?   _____

15. What does a driver have to do to park a car in a small and narrow garage?   _____

16. What describes something that you do because, all of a sudden, it just seems like a good idea?   _____

17. What could you use to explain to someone a deal you'd like to make with him or her?   _____

18. What describes both outer space and the love a dog has for its master?   _____

19. What threatens to separate people from their hats and umbrellas during a storm?   _____

Exercise D: Rhyme Time
Write the **Word** that best completes each rhyme.

20. Itsy-bitsy bugs are flying all around the fruit.
    Barely big enough to see, they really are ___.

    _____

21. My sister plays the drums; my brother plays the violin.
    And when they do, *I* play outside (but can't escape the ___).

    _____

22. When the pass soared toward Tommy, I grabbed it and kept it.
    No one had guessed that I might ___ it.

    _____

23. My brother's in a mood today, and all he does is growl.
    If I should glance his way, I know that I would see a ___.

    _____

24. She was going too fast. That is just undeniable.
    She caused the crash; it is she who is ___.

    _____

Exercise E: True or False
Circle TRUE or FALSE for each statement.

25. A hearing aid **hampers** one's ability to hear. . . . . . TRUE FALSE

26. You're **liable** to improve by practicing something. . . TRUE FALSE

27. Panda bears tend to have **wiry** bodies. . . . . TRUE FALSE

28. You **submerge** yourself when you dive into a pool. . TRUE FALSE

29. A **gale** of laughter would be hard to hear. . . . . TRUE FALSE

Exercise F: If . . .
Write the **Word** that best completes each sentence.

WEDNESDAY
Awful aroma near orchard. Dumb flies love it. One dummy asked how I'm able to maneuver from place to place so well since I don't have wings and am so minute. By ITCH-hiking, I said. Naturally. Flies are just so dumb!

30. If one criminal is shipping a load of stolen goods to another,
    this shipment is one that the police will try to . . . .

    _____

31. If you have a bad cold and are all stuffed up, you can see a
    flower's beauty but you might not be aware of its . . . .

    _____

32. If a basketball player dribbles to the right, then suddenly turns
    left and gets past someone who is blocking her, that's a good . . . .

    _____

33. If a pile of oily rags suddenly bursts into flame without being
    lit by a match (and this really can happen), that fire is . . . .

    _____

34. If you think of something fun to do but you need your friends
    to agree to do it, what you would present to them would be a . . . .

    _____

35. If you were in a new situation where everyone acted differently
    than you were used to, their way of doing things would seem . . . .

    _____

Exercise G: Fill-in

Write the Word that best completes each sentence. Use each word only once.

Quick LIST

alien ADJ., N.
aroma N.
boundless ADJ.
din N.
gale N.
hamper V.
intercept V.
liable ADJ.
maneuver N., V.
minute ADJ.
proposition N.
scowl V., N.
spontaneous ADJ.
submerge V.
wiry ADJ.

36. Imagine how _____ the first Europeans in the New World must have seemed to Native Americans.

37. What do you think of my _____ that I will cook dinner tonight if you will do the dishes?

38. When a home run is hit, we can hear the _____ from the stadium even though it's two blocks away.

39. Mom surprised and delighted us with her _____ purchase of a puppy that had caught her eye.

40. The scientist used a microscope to look at _____ differences between the two samples.

41. At a national border, customs officials try to _____ any goods are not supposed to enter that country.

42. A wheelchair can be awkward and difficult to _____, but I've become fairly good at it.

43. If you damage someone's property, you are _____ for repairing or replacing it.

44. Tree branches littered our yard after last night's _____.

45. I know a pumpkin pie is in the oven because its _____ fills the house.

46. A heavy backpack and a sore ankle combined to _____ me on the hike.

47. If I use bad manners in public, both of my parents _____ at me.

48. Out on the ocean, with no land in sight, the water seems _____.

49. Years of being a long-distance runner have given my dad a _____ build.

50. We hid the canoe at the lakeshore by filling it with rocks to _____ it.

THURSDAY
Was intercepted by some silly spider. "Come into my parlor," she said. Asked why don't I settle down. Why do I want to keep maneuvering around all the time and so on and so on. Well, I said, how else could I get from hair to there? Sheesh! Dumbness in the insect world just seems boundless! And the humans don't seem any too smart either!

FRIDAY
Met a pup. Plan to sleep all day. Good doggie.

Lesson 27

ascend *uh•SEND* VERB
to go up; to move upward [Let's *ascend* the mountain and picnic at the top.]

climax *KLY•max* NOUN
the time or part of anything that is of highest interest, importance, or excitement [The *climax* of the story involves the capture of the criminal.]

contrary *KON•trair•ee*
ADJECTIVE **1.** exactly opposite; completely different [We have *contrary* opinions on cats.]
ADJECTIVE **2.** opposed; being or acting against [Illegal actions are *contrary* to the law.]
ADJECTIVE **3.** hard to get along with; stubborn [He is a *contrary* child who must always have his own way.]
NOUN the opposite [The sun is not closer to Earth than the moon; the *contrary* is true.]

curb *KURB* VERB
to hold back, restrain, or control [Try to *curb* your anger by counting to ten.]

fatigue *fuh•TEEG*
NOUN weariness; exhaustion [I collapsed with *fatigue* after the race.]
VERB to make weary or exhausted [A ten-mile hike will *fatigue* us.]

gait *GATE* NOUN
a way of walking or running [With my sore ankle, I have a slow *gait*.]

horizontal *hor•uh•ZON•tul* ADJECTIVE
parallel to the horizon; level [Table tops are *horizontal*.]

intimate *IN•tih•mut* ADJECTIVE
1. very private or personal [I tell my best friend my *intimate* thoughts.]
2. close; very friendly [We get along well, but I wouldn't say that we're *intimate* friends.]

mutilate *MYOO•tih•late* VERB
to cut, tear, or break off a part; to badly damage or injure by cutting, tearing, or breaking off a part of [A lawn mower could *mutilate* a person's foot.]

precise *pree•SICE* ADJECTIVE
1. exact; accurate [Provide a *precise* answer, or you will get no credit.]
2. clear and definite [I gave *precise* instructions, so you should not have been confused.]
3. very careful in the way something is done; fussy [Mitch is always very *precise* in arranging his room.]

replica *REP•lih•kuh* NOUN
a copy or model, often smaller than the original [I have a coin bank that is a *replica* of the Liberty Bell.]

righteous *RY•chus* ADJECTIVE
1. decent; good; moral [Parents should raise their children to be *righteous* people.]
2. justified; with good reason; proper [When Leo saw any form of cruelty, he was filled with *righteous* anger.]

rile *RILE* VERB
to make angry; to irritate [Don't *rile* her by being so sassy.]

skeletal *SKEL•uh•tul*
ADJECTIVE of or like a skeleton [We found an animal's *skeletal* remains.]

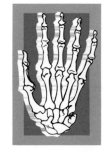

A skeletal image

weather *WETH•ur* VERB
1. to survive; to pass safely through a danger or hardship [Can our friendship *weather* this argument?]
2. to become worn or affected by being exposed to the weather [Some types of wood *weather* over time to a pale, silvery color.]

Exercise A: Yes or No

Circle YES or NO for each question.

1. Would you feel shy and awkward around an **intimate** friend? . . . . . .   YES   NO
2. If you **weather** an illness, do you recover? . . . .   YES   NO
3. Could a dog **mutilate** a teddy bear by chewing off its ears? . . . . . .   YES   NO
4. Does a story's **climax** come near the beginning? . . . .   YES   NO
5. Would it **rile** your mother if you gave her a thoughtful gift? . . . . .   YES   NO
6. Do dieters try to **curb** their appetites? . . . .   YES   NO
7. Is protecting a small child from a big bully a **righteous** act? . . . . . .   YES   NO

Exercise B: What Is It?

Write the Word that each clue describes.

8. This describes a horse that won't go when you want it to but keeps going when you say "Whoa."   _____

9. This could be a trot, a limp, a gallop, a steady walk, or a way of hopping.   _____

10. This describes a time, such as 5:14 P.M. or a height, such as 63.25 inches.   _____

11. This describes the top of a plateau, the floor of a bowling alley, and most ceilings.   _____

12. This is what the sun, wind, and a dry climate do to someone's skin over time.   _____

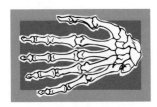

A horizontal view of the previous skeletal image

Exercise C: Completion

Choose the correct answer to complete each sentence.

_____ 13. One **gait** used by horses is a
   A. corral.   B. gallop.   C. saddle.

_____ 14. Something that people **ascend** is
   A. stairs.   B. scissors.   C. a nod.

_____ 15. One thing that is always true of any **replica** is that it is NOT
   A. cheap.   B. attractive.   C. the "real thing."

_____ 16. A person who has a **skeletal** appearance looks
   A. old.   B. very thin.   C. strong.

_____ 17. One thing that is likely to **fatigue** people is
   A. hard work.   B. a good book.   C. exciting plans.

Exercise D: Synonyms

Write the **Word** that could be used in place of each underlined word or phrase.

18. Please hold the ladder very steady while I <u>climb</u> it.

_____

19. Our relationship is so <u>trusting and affectionate</u> that we have almost no secrets from each other.

_____

20. Politeness may require people to <u>keep down</u> the desire to tell others what they really think.

_____

21. This looks just like a baseball card from 1920, but it's not a real one; it's a <u>duplicate</u>.

_____

22. Katie listened to her conscience, so we can count on her to do what is <u>honorable</u>.

_____

23. It's hard for me to keep up with Simon's quick and long-legged <u>steps</u>.

_____

24. My neighbor is the most impossible, grumpy, <u>difficult</u> man I've ever known.

_____

25. The doctor is not sure that the patient can <u>last through</u> the surgery.

_____

26. My <u>great tiredness</u> kept me from being able to go any farther.

_____

27. The <u>high point</u> of the play had all of us on the edge of our seats.

_____

28. To do this exercise, you should be in a <u>flat</u> position on the floor.

_____

29. Oh, don't say that unless you want to <u>really annoy</u> him.

_____

Exercise E: Antonyms

Write the **Word** that is an antonym for each set of words.

30. chubby; well-fed; fat

_____

31. encourage; urge; awaken; inspire

_____

32. similar; in agreement with; alike

_____

33. sink; fall; lessen; plunge

_____

34. careless; foggy; general; loose

_____

35. heal; repair; mend

_____

What goes up
must come down.
Anything that ascends
must also do the contrary.

Exercise F: Fill-in

Write the Word that best completes each sentence. Use each word only once.

36. If a roof is completely _____, snow won't slide off it.

37. The small fishing boat was not able to _____ the storm, and it sank.

38. During the _____ of that movie, the hero discovered who the murderer was and captured him.

39. Breakfast doesn't come after lunch; the _____ is true!

40. Please don't _____ the encyclopedia by tearing articles out of it.

41. I used an elevator to _____ to the fourth floor but walked back down.

42. If you _____ a rattlesnake, it is likely to try to bite you.

43. Even a short walk would _____ my grandfather while he was sick.

44. The woman's _____ was so brisk that I had to jog to keep up with her.

45. The government sent troops to try to _____ the rebellion.

46. Don't ask for _____ details about my life; they are none of your business.

47. We were worried about the kitten's _____ condition, but he gained weight with a healthy diet.

48. Our science project was a small _____ of a volcano.

49. Please be _____ when you set the table; make sure the silverware is lined up perfectly.

50. Meg thought feeding the hungry was such a _____ cause that she spent her entire allowance on canned goods for the food collection.

Different activities require different gaits.

Quick LIST

	curb V.	intimate ADJ.	righteous ADJ.
ascend V.	fatigue N., V.	mutilate V.	rile V.
climax N.	gait N.	precise ADJ.	skeletal ADJ.
contrary ADJ., N.	horizontal ADJ.	replica N.	weather V.

Lesson 28 _____

arrogant *AIR•uh•gunt* ADJECTIVE
overly proud; conceited; full of feelings of
importance ["I'll win, of course," said Hank in an
arrogant voice.]

callous *KAL•us* ADJECTIVE
feeling no emotion, especially sympathy
[I don't understand how you can be so *callous*
about my suffering.]

crafty *KRAF•tee* ADJECTIVE
skillful in fooling or tricking others; sly; sneaky
[Don't trust a *crafty* person.]

dejected *dih•JEK•tud* ADJECTIVE
sad; discouraged [Cyrus felt *dejected* when he
didn't make the team.]

domestic *duh•MES•tik* ADJECTIVE
1. having to do with the home or family
[Everyone should have *domestic* skills such as
cooking.]
2. having to do with, or made in, one's own
country; native [Hal bought a *domestic* car, but
Cal bought an import.]
3. not wild; having to do with animals that are
used to living with or near people [Both cows
and chickens are *domestic* animals.]

Although most kinds of
mice are *not* domestic
animals, the ones
that we call
"house mice"
are certainly
used to living
with people.

entice *en•TICE* VERB
to attract or tempt by offering something that
is wanted [I tried to *entice* the shy puppy
to come to me by holding out a bone.]

err *UR* or *AIR* VERB
to make a mistake; to do something wrong
[If you *err*, do your best to correct what you have
done.]

hardy *HAR•dee* ADJECTIVE
able to survive great hardship; physically
tough [Are you *hardy* enough to do a ten-mile hike
today?]

lavish *LAV•ish*
ADJECTIVE **1.** very generous or too generous
[Her *lavish* gifts embarrassed him.]
ADJECTIVE **2.** more than enough; very great
[I can't eat such a *lavish* helping.]
VERB to give or spend freely or too freely
[My next-door neighbors *lavish* attention on all
their cats.]

modify *MOD•uh•fy* VERB
1. to make a small or partial change [I'll
modify my report to include more details.]
2. to tone down; to make less harsh or strong
[I wish the teacher would *modify* the
requirements for this paper.]

orator *OR•uh•tur* NOUN
a skillful, public speaker; someone who gives
a formal speech [The *orator* grabbed our
attention with her opening sentence.]

paramount *PAIR•uh•mownt* ADJECTIVE
most important; supreme; ranking higher than
any other [Our *paramount* concern is safety.]

prosperity *pros•PAIR•uh•tee* NOUN
good fortune, wealth, and success [We have
been blessed with great *prosperity*.]

Some people think of mice as cute little
critters; others see them as crafty
rogues.

rogue *ROAG* NOUN
1. a dishonest or tricky person [That *rogue* has
managed to fool us all.]
2. someone who is playful in a mischievous
way [That little *rogue* cut the toes out of my socks!]

threadbare *THRED•bair* ADJECTIVE
worn out, shabby [I need a new coat; this one is
threadbare.]

Exercise A: Antonyms
Write the Word that is an antonym for each set of words.

1. delicate; fragile _____

2. poverty; hardship _____

3. humble; shy _____

4. sensitive; tender _____

5. honest; open _____

6. foreign; imported _____

7. least; slightest _____

8. inadequate; scarce _____

Question:
What do mice call their king and queen?

Answer:
The paramount pair o' mice

Exercise B: Synonyms
Write the Word that is a synonym for each set of words.

9. coax; persuade _____

10. adjust; revise _____

11. sneaky; dishonest _____

12. rascal; villain _____

13. hardhearted; unfeeling _____

14. goof; blunder; mess up _____

15. stuck-up; scornful _____

16. chief; main; greatest _____

17. sorrowful; unhappy _____

18. strong; healthy; fit _____

Exercise C:
Other Forms of Words
Use what you know about the Words to choose the correct answers.

____ 19. A dog might express **dejection** by
A. snarling.
B. whimpering.
C. wagging its tail.

____ 20. An animal that has been **domesticated** is one that has been
A. tamed.
B. hunted.
C. captured.

____ 21. People show **arrogance** when they act as if they are
A. shy.
B. superior.
C. insulted.

____ 22. A **prosperous** store is one that is
A. doing well.
B. part of a chain.
C. going out of business.

____ 23. An animal that is known for its **craftiness** is the
A. pig.
B. fox.
C. mule.

"Doncha think the answer ta 23 oughtta be mouse?"

Exercise D: Yes or No

Circle YES or NO for each question.

24. In the drawings in this lesson, do the mice look **dejected**? . . . .   YES   NO

25. Might **threadbare** clothing soon need to be patched? . . . .   YES   NO

26. Is a bribe used to **entice** someone to do something? . . . .   YES   NO

27. If you **err** throughout a test, will you get an A? . . . .   YES   NO

28. Does an **orator** need a band or orchestra? . . . .   YES   NO

Exercise E: Rhyme Time

Write the Word that is described by each rhyme.

"Doncha wanna dance with me?"

29. This person speaks so well (and never mutters)
    That people hang on every word he utters.

    _____

30. This describes a rug or shirt or an upholstered chair
    That's had its surface worn away and is the worse for wear.

    _____

31. Cooking and washing and sweeping the floor
    All are examples of this kind of chore.

    _____

32. If you want to be this, if you want to be sturdy,
    You'd better eat more than the average birdie.

    _____

33. This really isn't someone to rely on.
    It's someone whom you'd better keep your eye on!

    _____

34. This describes the gifts the princess got—
    Three cars, a house, eight diamonds, and a yacht!

    _____

35. You'd do this to a pancake recipe
    If you put in two eggs instead of three.

    _____

"Doncha think ya could maybe write about *me*?"

Exercise F: Writing

Think about the mice you know from cartoons, movies, and stories, and think about real, live mice. Then, on your own paper, write a very short mouse story. You may write about storybook mice or real ones, about one mouse or a whole bunch of them. Use at least THREE Words in your story.

Quick LIST

arrogant ADJ.	**dejected** ADJ.	**err** V.	**modify** V.	**prosperity** N.
callous ADJ.	**domestic** ADJ.	**hardy** ADJ.	**orator** N.	**rogue** N.
crafty ADJ.	**entice** V.	**lavish** ADJ., V.	**paramount** ADJ.	**threadbare** ADJ.

Exercise G: Fill-in

Write the Word that best completes each sentence. Use each word only once.

36. Rudy left a pie on the outside windowsill to cool, and some _____ came along and stole it!

37. The antique dealer cheated people with a _____ plan to sell cleverly made copies of valuable, old objects.

38. Jeff's allowance is so _____ that he always has more money than any of the rest of us.

39. I'm preparing a lot of food because I'd rather _____ by having too much for my guests than too little.

40. After years of struggling, our family began a time of _____ when both of my parents found well-paying jobs.

41. The pioneers had to be very _____ folk to make the long journey west by wagon train.

42. The _____ woman acted as if her opinions and ideas were the only ones that mattered.

43. When I broke my finger, my teacher agreed to _____ her requirement that my papers be neatly written.

44. President John F. Kennedy was a great _____ whose speeches are still quoted today.

45. After striking out, the batter looked _____ as he sat down and slumped against the fence.

46. We used tuna fish to _____ the lost cat to come into our house.

Question: Why would one put cheese in a trap?

Aswer: To entice mice

47. People who buy _____ products help to support American businesses.

48. The _____ cause of our losing the game was that we had never practiced.

49. After years of wear and tear, our _____ sofa really needs to be replaced.

50. A person would have to be pretty _____ to ignore the cry of a frightened child.

"Doncha think a good cheese pizza would be a lot nicer?"

Lesson 29

amiable *AY•mee•uh•bul* ADJECTIVE
good-natured and friendly [My neighbor always greets me with an *amiable* smile.]

dismantle *dis•MAN•tul* VERB
to take apart, temporarily or permanently [If we *dismantle* the bed, we can get it upstairs.]

emphasis *EM•fuh•sis* NOUN
1. stress; importance [At our school, the *emphasis* is on reading.]
2. a special force or stress put on particular words or syllables [Put *emphasis* on the first syllable in *desert* or you will mispronounce it.]

excessive *ek•SES•iv* ADJECTIVE
being too much or too great; going beyond what is usual or proper [Four hours of homework a night seems *excessive* to me.]

flaw *FLAW*
NOUN   a fault or imperfection in a thing or person [The only *flaw* in the plate was a small crack.]
VERB   to make or become imperfect (most often used with -*ed*) [The play was *flawed* by one actor's poor performance.]

FLAWED   NOT

heed *HEED* VERB
to give close attention to; to take notice of [I will *heed* your advice.]

intensify *in•TEN•suh•fy* VERB
to make stronger or more serious; to increase [We must *intensify* our efforts.]

lofty *LOF•tee* ADJECTIVE
very high [The eagle looked down from its *lofty* nest above the valley.]

modesty *MOD•us•tee* NOUN
1. the quality of not thinking too highly of oneself [Spencer's *modesty* about his accomplishments kept him from bragging.]
2. the quality of not calling attention to one's body [In earlier days, *modesty* in women's clothing was very important.]

momentary *MOH•mun•tair•ee* ADJECTIVE
lasting only a moment; short-lived [There was a *momentary* pause.]

solitary *SOL•uh•tair•ee* ADJECTIVE
1. all alone; apart from others [A *solitary* child watched the others playing.]
2. single; only [The *solitary* tree in my yard provides little shade.]
3. seldom visited; lonely [The *solitary* house was set in the woods.]

subtle *SUT•tul* ADJECTIVE
1. not open; not very noticeable [Laura gave me a *subtle* wink that no one else spotted.]
2. delicate; faint [That perfume has a pleasant, *subtle* smell.]

turmoil *TUR•moil* NOUN
a very excited or confused condition; commotion [During a riot, there is *turmoil*.]

twinge *TWINJ* NOUN
1. a sudden, brief pain [If I put even a little weight on my twisted ankle, I feel a *twinge*.]
2. a sudden, brief feeling of regret, shame, guilt or other negative feeling [Sue felt a *twinge* of jealousy when Mara won the contest.]

visualize *VIZH•oo•uh•lize* VERB
to form a mental image or picture of something [Can you *visualize* how the room would look with bunk beds?]

Exercise A: *If . . .*

Write the **Word** that best completes each sentence.

1. If you don't try to be the center of attention, and if you think the good things you do are what anyone would do, you have . . .   _____

2. If you wear a hat, mittens, a scarf, two sweaters, and a coat on a mild day, your clothing is . . . .   _____

3. If you're a new student and the others welcome you, show an interest in you, and ask you to join them for lunch, they're . . .   _____

4. If a woman lives by herself and doesn't have company and doesn't go out to mix with other people, her life is . . . .   _____

5. If you read a list of rules and one is in capital letters and ends with an exclamation point, that rule has a special . . . .   _____

6. If someone says to you, "Do *not*, for any reason, *ever . . . ,*" what follows is something the person really wants you to . . . . . .   _____

7. If you forgot you had a sore tooth and you bit down on a pretzel, you would feel a . . . .   _____

8. If your parents were buying a used car, they would drive it and look at it carefully in order to notice any . . . .   _____

Exercise B: Completion

Choose the correct answer to complete each sentence.

____ 9. You might communicate with your mother in a **subtle** way by
   A. shrieking.   B. jumping.   C. nudging her.

____ 10. A shirt would be **flawed** by
   A. stains.   B. buttons.   C. ironing.

____ 11. A person with **modesty** does not
   A. brag.   B. tell jokes.   C. take risks.

____ 12. An example of a **lofty** building is a
   A. fort.   B. shack.   C. skyscraper.

____ 13. You could **intensify** the warmth of a campfire by
   A. putting it out.   B. adding wood.   C. moving away from it.

SOLITARY OR NOT?

Exercise C: Synonyms

Write the Word that is a synonym for each word.

14. disturbance _____

15. towering _____

16. strengthen _____

17. kind _____

18. imagine _____

Exercise D: Other Forms of Words

Use what you know about the Words to choose the correct answers.

____ 19. A **modest** woman in the 1800s would *not* have wanted people to notice her
    A. legs.
    B. house.
    C. hat.

____ 20. Which is the most **emphatic** way to say no to a request?
    A. "I don't think I can."
    B. "Uh . . . no."
    C. "Not in a million years!"

____ 21. It is most foolish to be **heedless** when you are given a
    A. compliment.
    B. warning.
    C. snack.

____ 22. What would be needed during the **dismantlement** of a swing set?
    A. paint
    B. screws and bolts
    C. a wrench and pliers

____ 23. If you turned in a **flawless** paper, what grade would you expect?
    A. an A
    B. a C
    C. an F

Exercise E: Analogies

Choose the word that completes the analogy.

____ 24. **visualize** : *mind* :: *smell* :
    A. odor   C. sense
    B. nose   D. notice

____ 25. *enough* : **excessive** :: *warm* :
    A. hot   C. sunny
    B. cold   D. ordinary

____ 26. **momentary** : *brief* :: *risky* :
    A. long   C. stupid
    B. quick   D. dangerous

____ 27. *pain* : **twinge** :: *look* :
    A. eyes   C. glance
    B. stare   D. suffering

Exercise F: Antonyms

Write the Word that is an antonym for each of these words.

28. low _____

29. ignore _____

30. endless _____

31. assemble _____

32. numerous _____

33. unfriendly _____

34. obvious _____

35. peace _____

A fly and a flea in a flue *
Were imprisoned, so what could they do?
   Said the fly, "Let us flee."
   Said the flea, "Let us fly."
So they flew through a flaw in the flue.

*A *flue* is a metal pipe that lines the inside of a chimney.

Exercise G: Fill-in

Write the Word that best completes each sentence. Use each word only once.

36. Can you _____ what a flying car would be like?

37. It is much more attractive to show some _____ than to act like you're so great.

38. "On my team," said the coach, "the _____ is on the basics, not the flashy plays."

39. Rita felt a _____ of regret about her decision, but it was too late to change her mind.

40. Schools have fire drills to avoid _____ if there is ever a real fire.

41. Turn down the radio, please; the volume is _____.

42. The only _____ in the tablecloth was one tiny hole.

43. Some animals live in groups, but some are _____ creatures.

44. Just a pinch of herbs will give the stew a _____ and interesting flavor.

45. My grandfather is so _____ that everyone feels comfortable around him.

46. We did not _____ the sign, "Slippery When Wet," and skidded into a ditch.

47. After a _____ delay while the screen went black, the film began again.

48. We need to _____ our search, so put out a call for more helpers.

49. In order to replace the part, we will need to _____ the engine.

50. From our _____ position, we could see for miles.

LOFTY

NOT

_____

Quick LIST

amiable ADJ.	**lofty** ADJ.
dismantle V.	**modesty** N.
emphasis N.	**momentary** ADJ.
excessive ADJ.	**solitary** ADJ.
flaw N., V.	**subtle** ADJ.
heed V.	**turmoil** N.
intensify V.	**twinge** N.
	visualize V.

HEED

DID NOT

Lesson 30 _____

affix *uh•FIX* VERB

to fasten, stick, or attach   [*Affix* the stamp to the envelope.]

aftermath *AF•tur•math* NOUN

1. a result, especially an unpleasant one [War's *aftermath* is misery.]

2. the period following an event of some importance   [In the *aftermath* of the election, protestors crowded the streets.]

deceitful *duh•SEET•ful* ADJECTIVE

lying; misleading; untruthful; false   [The salesman was accused of *deceitful* claims.]

deplete *duh•PLEET* VERB

to make less by using up gradually; to partly or completely empty   [I don't want to *deplete* my savings by buying things I don't need.]

discontent *dis•kun•TENT* NOUN

a feeling of not being satisfied; a desire for something more or different   [Her *discontent* made her restless.]

indelible *in•DEL•uh•bul* ADJECTIVE

unable to be erased, removed, or blotted out [This stain won't wash out; it must have been made by *indelible* ink.]

insufferable *in•SUF•ur•uh•bul* ADJECTIVE

hard to put up with; unbearable   [His constant complaining was *insufferable*.]

inventory *IN•vun•tor•ee*

NOUN   1. a complete list of goods, valuables, or property   [Let's do an *inventory* of supplies.]

NOUN   2. the stock of goods on hand   [The school's *inventory* of athletic equipment is small.]

VERB   to count or make a list of inventory [The store will *inventory* everything it has in the warehouse.]

meditate *MED•uh•tate* VERB

to think quietly and deeply   [I like to look up at the sky and *meditate* about my future.]

"This is Mary Sue Moss. Today we're asking folks on the street about 'Rules for Life' that could make the world a better place. Later we'll ask for *your* ideas. Stay tuned!"

revert *ruh• VERT* VERB

to go back to a former condition, subject, or way of acting; to return   [After working hard for a few weeks, he began to *revert* to his old, lazy ways.]

sheepish *SHEE•pish* ADJECTIVE

embarrassed, especially over having a mistake or fault revealed   [The woman apologized with a *sheepish* smile.]

sulky *SUL•kee* ADJECTIVE

silent and gloomy because of being angry or upset   [He always gets *sulky* when he doesn't get his own way.]

teem *TEEM* VERB

to be full of; to swarm   [In another month, this quiet camp will *teem* with activity and happy kids.]

tolerant *TOL•ur•unt* ADJECTIVE

showing acceptance of others' opinions, beliefs, or customs, even though they are not like one's own   [To get along with others, one must be *tolerant*.]

waylay *WAY•lay* VERB

1. to lie in wait for; to wait for and attack [There are dangerous robbers who *waylay* travelers along that trail.]

2. to wait for and stop a person on his or her way   [I will try to *waylay* a player and get her autograph as she arrives for the game.]

Exercise A: Completion

Choose the correct answer for each question.

_____ 1. People tend to feel *sheepish* about doing something
   A. hard.   B. foolish.   C. admirable.

_____ 2. You *deplete* your food supply by
   A. eating.   B. shopping.   C. refrigerating it.

_____ 3. The *aftermath* of a tornado is
   A. strong wind.   B. destruction.   C. a funnel cloud.

_____ 4. You *inventory* your school supplies to check what you
   A. have.   B. use.   C. can afford.

_____ 5. Sidewalks that *teem* with people are
   A. empty.   B. slippery.   C. crowded.

_____ 6. If someone is being *insufferable*, you're likely to say,
   A. "Thanks."   B. "Stop it."   C. "I'm sorry."

_____ 7. Your thoughts *revert* to something when you
   A. plan.   B. daydream.   C. remember.

Exercise B: If . . .

Write the Word that best completes each sentence.

8. If you angrily accuse someone of taking something of yours
   and then you find it right where you'd left it under your bed,
   your apology will probably be . . . .   _____

9. If workers in a warehouse count every box and can and object
   and write down the results, they are probably taking . . . .   _____

10. If a child who has misbehaved is told to sit in the corner and
    think about what he or she has done, the child is supposed to . . . . .   _____

11. If you were bored silly at a picnic that had lots of mosquitoes
    and little food, you might say that your afternoon was . . . .   _____

12. If things aren't working out and you want things you can't have
    and you just don't feel peaceful and happy, you have a sense of . . .   _____

13. If someone makes such an impression on you that you never
    forget the person, he or she has made an impression that is . . . .   _____

14. If you believe in "live and let live" and accept people's differ-
    ences and don't make harsh judgments about others, you are . . . . .   _____

"I'll waylay this gentleman. Oh, I know you. It's Bob, isn't it? What rule can you share with our TV audience?"

"Um, let me meditate on that. . . . Um, I think one should affix one's hat, er, firmly. Oh, yes, it's Bob."

"I'm on TV? Oh, I'm sure this will prove to be an indelible experience. My sister in Omaha will— What? . . . How could I have depleted my time? . . . Oh."

Exercise C: Synonyms

Write the Word that is a synonym for each set of words.

15. annoying; irritating; horrible _____

16. decrease; drain; reduce _____

17. lasting; permanent _____

18. ashamed; guilty _____

19. halt; ambush _____

20. glum; moody _____

21. dishonest; sneaky _____

22. connect; join; paste _____

23. open-minded; understanding _____

"I am Osgood, and my rule is 'Apologize sheepishly if you've been baaaaaaad!' Hee-hee! Get it?"

"My advice to everyone is to watch out! The world is teeming with insufferable twerps! I won't mention any names."

Exercise D: What Is It?

Write the Word that each clue describes.

24. This is what people do if they outgrow some behavior but then start it again. _____

25. This is what hives do when bees are busy and school halls do when the bell rings. _____

26. This is what people do when they're "lost in thought" about something important. _____

27. This is what reporters try to do to famous people when they want to question them. _____

28. This describes people who pout, act grumpy, and insist on being left alone. _____

29. This describes liars, cheaters, spies, and people who wear disguises. _____

Exercise E: Antonyms

Write the correct Word to complete each sentence.
This exercise continues on the next page.

30. The opposite of "to improve, progress, or advance" is to . . . . . . _____

31. The opposite of a feeling of satis-faction and pleasure is one of . . . . _____

_____

Quick LIST

affix V.
aftermath N.
deceitful ADJ.
deplete V.
discontent N.
indelible ADJ.
insufferable ADJ.
inventory N., V.
meditate V.
revert V.
sheepish ADJ.
sulky ADJ.
teem V.
tolerant ADJ.
waylay V.

32. The opposite of what happens
    before something is its .... _____

33. The opposite of a list of what's
    been sold or used up is an ...... _____

34. The opposite of "to loosen,
    remove, or separate" is to .... _____

35. The opposite of being cheerful,
    chatty, and bright is being .... _____

Exercise F: Fill-in

Write the Word that best completes each sentence. Use each word only once.

36. If we _____ labels, we'll know what's in the jars.

37. I feared someone might _____ me in the dark alley.

38. I love fishing in Montana where the rivers _____ with trout.

39. Raul gave me a _____ look as he admitted how wrong he'd been.

40. That story's effect was so _____ that it has always stayed with me.

41. I wish Homer would stop being so _____ and get in a good mood.

42. The more wood and paper we use, the more we _____ our forests.

43. If you have a reputation for being _____, people won't trust you.

44. When you stay at other people's homes, you must be _____ of the
    way they do things.

45. I'll never baby-sit for those _____ brats again; they run
    wild, sass me constantly, and try their best to drive me crazy.

46. Filled with _____ about my appearance, I started
    exercising and got a haircut.

47. If you ignore your garden, it will _____ to the
    wild patch of weeds it once was.

48. The store keeps track of its _____ and can, there-
    fore, order new stock when it's needed.

49. I always make better decisions if I _____ about
    them for a while.

50. The _____ of picnicking in a patch of poison ivy
    was that we all came down with itchy rashes.

"I shay don't inventory yer chickensh before they hatch. Now, I'd be glad to fetch shomethin for ya? . . . Ya sure?"

Word Fun 6!

Digging

Find and underline the **Word** from Unit 6 that's buried in each sentence. These are the words you need to dig up:

din	entice	flaw	inventory	rile
discontent	err	gale	revert	twinge

1. My goodness, it's so loud in here!

2. That writer really made a dumb mistake.

3. When my twin gets a cramp, I feel a sharp pain myself.

4. A strong wind blew my wig a lengthy way down the street.

5. I hope my pet wolf will never ever turn back to his wild ways.

6. When I saw the advertisement, I certainly wanted to buy that toy!

7. List all of the things you invent, or you won't know what you have.

8. My complaint is that you have had the same compact disc on ten times!

9. Sure, my reaction is anger. I let you borrow my bike, and you broke it!

10. Have you heard of laws to protect buyers from purchasing products that aren't perfect?

The Twins

My Pet

A. Lee Enn

Naming

Match each person's name to the description it goes best with.

____	1. N. Tyce	A.	He makes you want whatever he's selling.
____	2. Cal Luss	B.	He's here one second and gone the next.
____	3. X. Essive	C.	She can really get around skillfully.
____	4. A. Lee Enn	D.	She just doesn't know when to stop.
____	5. Ma Noover	E.	You won't meet a nicer person.
____	6. Sol Uhterry	F.	She's just a sneaky little liar.
____	7. O. Ray Turr	G.	He's pretty much of a loner.
____	8. Dee Seetfull	H.	What a great speaker he is!
____	9. Amy Uhbull	I.	He's not from around here.
____	10. Moe Menterry	J.	He is so insensitive!

Puzzling

Identify the **Word** from Unit 6 that fits the clue in each box.
The word's first letter is shown in the answer blank.

stuck ↑	1. a _____
GOOF ∩P	2. e _____
Up! Down! Right! Left! Yes! No! Now! Later! In! Out!	3. c _____
	4. i _____

feeling ↓	5. d _____
VERY THIN	6. s _____
GO UNDER	7. s _____
tiny	8. m _____

Rhyming

These poems would be better if they rhymed. Substitute a **Word**
from Unit 6 for each underlined phrase to make the line rhyme
with the one above it.

1. Crashing to the ground is surely going to be my fate
    Unless the horse I'm riding starts to use a smoother <u>way of running</u>!   _____

2. I can't imagine ever being dogless, poochless, houndless.
    My love for Man's Best Friend, you see, is absolutely <u>without limits</u>.   _____

3. When doing math, it's my advice
    To check your work and be <u>completely accurate</u>.   _____

Word Fun Answers!

Unit 1, pages 38–39

MATCHING
1.	H	6.	E
2.	I	7.	J
3.	C	8.	G
4.	F	9.	D
5.	B	10.	A

BOXING
1.	sla<u>v</u>e	V
2.	s<u>o</u>b	O
3.	<u>c</u>heer	C
4.	cow<u>a</u>rd	A
5.	<u>b</u>ully	B
6.	shr<u>ug</u>	U
7.	p<u>l</u>ease	L
8.	m<u>a</u>nsion	A
9.	desse<u>r</u>t	R
10.	m<u>y</u>stery	Y

PUZZLING
1. cower
2. ponder
3. illuminate
4. endure *or* persevere
5. insufficient
6. trivial
7. immense

RHYMING
1. acute
2. futile

Unit 2, pages 60–61

DIGGING
1. <u>host, I left</u>
   hostile
2. di<u>sh under</u>
   shun
3. re<u>cord, I al</u>ways
   cordial
4. si<u>p. Archery</u>
   parch
5. crow<u>d is. Hear ten</u>
   dishearten
6. arithmeti<u>c on fine</u>
   confine
7. score<u>d a zero</u>
   daze
8. we<u>re el</u>astic
   reel

MATCHING
1.	B	5.	G
2.	H	6.	A
3.	E	7.	F
4.	D	8.	C

NAMING
1.	D	6.	H
2.	I	7.	E
3.	F	8.	G
4.	A	9.	J
5.	B	10.	C

RHYMING
1. glutton
2. opinionated

PUZZLING
1. monotonous
2. dilute
3. cycle

Unit 3, pages 82–83

PUZZLING
1. exclude
2. decade
3. chaos
4. sever
5. blunder
6. gorge
7. belated
8. incentive
9. erect
10. fundamental

SEARCHING
1.	strong	
2.	hug	
3.	fair	
4.	eat	
5.	read	*How many*
6.	mud	*other words*
7.	joy	*did you*
8.	dent	*find?*

NAMING
1.	H	6.	I
2.	E	7.	A
3.	C	8.	G
4.	F	9.	B
5.	D		

DEFINING
1.	C	6.	D
2.	E	7.	I
3.	H	8.	B
4.	G	9.	F
5.	A		

RHYMING
1. repentance
2. remote

Unit 4, pages 104–105

PUZZLING
1. conspicuous
2. urgent
3. pursue
4. dwindle
5. immune
6. hover

CROSSING
1. (across) pauper
1. (down) plight
2. (across) tyrant
3. (down) resent

NAMING

1.	F	6.	E
2.	H	7.	J
3.	D	8.	G
4.	I	9.	A
5.	B	10.	C

DIGGING
1. Ski<u>p ran kh</u>aki
   prank
2. seein<u>g a pec</u>uliar
   gape
3. <u>ball, you</u>
   ally
4. usin<u>g our method</u>
   gourmet
5. tea<u>m, or a le</u>sser
   morale
6. <u>tag, I leap</u>
   agile
7. the<u>m in glee</u>
   mingle
8. <u>Bill owes</u>
   billow

RHYMING
1. fleet
2. plight
3. query
4. terse

Unit 5, pages 126–127

PUZZLING
1. writhe
2. pessimist
3. optimist
4. bliss
5. sparse
6. cluster
7. luminous

NAMING

1.	C	4.	A
2.	D	5.	B
3.	E		

MATCHING

1.	C	7.	J
2.	L	8.	H
3.	F	9.	G
4.	E	10.	B
5.	A	11.	D
6.	I	12.	K

DEFINING

1.	B	4.	E
2.	C	5.	D
3.	A		

A-MAZE-ING
1. (right) memorable
2. (down) extinguish
3. (left) haphazard
4. (up) dilemma
5. (right) alter
6. (down) rational

Unit 6, pages 148–149

DIGGING
1. lou<u>d in</u>
   din
2. writ<u>er really</u>
   err
3. <u>twin gets</u>
   twinge
4. wi<u>g a lengthy</u>
   gale
5. neve<u>r ever tu</u>rn
   revert
6. advertise<u>ment, I cer</u>tainly
   entice
7. <u>invent, or you</u>
   inventory
8. <u>disc on ten</u> times
   discontent
9. <u>anger. I let</u>
   rile
10. o<u>f law</u>
    flaw

NAMING

1.	A	6.	G
2.	J	7.	H
3.	D	8.	F
4.	I	9.	E
5.	C	10.	B

PUZZLING
1. arrogant
2. err
3. contrary
4. intensify
5. dejected
6. skeletal
7. submerge
8. minute

RHYMING
1. gait
2. boundless
3. precise

Word Index

Question:

How would you convey a pig to the hospital?

Answer: By ham-bulance

Question:
Why are elephants
on beaches intolerable?

Answer: Because they
can't keep their trunks up.

"It's Mary Sue Moss, submerged in the lake today *[gurgle]* to talk to . . ."

Good, you have finished the book!

What? You haven't? Well, then, why are you reading this? Go to page 40 and study the definition of the word *studious*. Right now.

I would very much like to hear from those who *have* completed their lessons. You may write to me, if you like, and tell me about things like:

- what you enjoyed about **Words to Go!**
- what you didn't enjoy (Though I simply can't imagine what that could be.)
- whether you found any mistakes
- which was your favorite joke or picture
- which kind of exercise you enjoyed most
- what you think is the best word of all the 450 words you learned
- what Rules for Life you wrote in Lesson 30

Goodness, now, don't tell me all of these things! You're probably busy, just like I am. After all, I have a classroom of my own to take care of, you know. But I certainly would love to hear from you.

If you write, please tell me your name, your grade, and your school's name. Send your letter to me at this address:

Mrs. Morgenstern
Perfection Learning
10520 New York Avenue
Des Moines, Iowa 50322-3775